W9-ARD-317

HUNTINGTON LIBRARY

PUBLICATIONS

THE MIDDLE ENGLISH MIRACLES
OF THE VIRGIN

THE
MIDDLE ENGLISH
MIRACLES
OF THE VIRGIN

BY BEVERLY BOYD

THE HUNTINGTON LIBRARY · 1964

SAN MARINO, CALIFORNIA

Copyright 1964
Henry E. Huntington Library and Art Gallery
Library of Congress Catalogue Card Number 63-13992

✧

Printed in the United States of America
by Princeton University Press, Princeton, New Jersey

PREFACE

THIS volume provides for students of Middle English literature, and for specialists in that field, an opportunity to explore a type of narrative that was extremely popular in England during the later Middle Ages. Best known to us through Chaucer's tale of the little clergeon slain by Jews, the miracles of the Virgin have attracted more interest in connection with the "Prioress's Tale" than they have attracted as specimens of Middle English verse and prose. While numerous essays have been written about them, there has been no comprehensive study of the genre itself and its place in our early literature.

I have tried, in these pages, to account for every miracle of the Virgin extant in Middle English, but I have not edited all of the tales. This is not because there would have been too many items; the book could have been expanded to include all of them. Because some tales are fragments too badly mutilated to be read, while others are repetitions of identical themes, and still others are trivialities scarcely worth anyone's attention, I have edited a representative selection only and summarized the rest in my notes, in all cases referring the reader to editions already in print. This procedure has enabled me to include nearly all of the independent tales and to deal with collections of miracles of the Virgin by selecting items which seem to me typical of their sources. These materials have been arranged in approximately chronological order (that of the manuscripts except when authors' dates are known). My notes have been designed to acquaint the reader with the collections from which some of the tales are drawn, as well as with the items chosen to represent them. The Introduction provides a brief history of the genre from its origins to its demise in England at the end of the Middle Ages. The Appendixes list items which are essentially translations, though Caxton's *Golden Legend* is represented in my texts because of its importance in the history of English literature.

The present state of the editions already in print has long demanded some such project as this. Many are scattered about in periodicals, and a great deal of the scholarship that has been done in the past is written in languages other than English. Few editions have good notes on the legends, and some are obsolete. I have tried to bring mine within the reach of anyone who has had a first course in Chaucer's works—the usual vehicle for introducing people to Middle English. I have endeavored to make these texts as accessible as possible without sacrificing the scribal spelling.

To do this, I have departed somewhat from the usual editorial policies of my predecessors in order to follow the procedures established by F. N. Robinson in his widely used editions of Chaucer's works (Boston, 1933 and 1957). Therefore, modern English punctuation and capitalization have been used, scribal abbreviations have been silently expanded, and the letters *i, j, u,* and *v* have been normalized. In addition, the symbol *þ* has been removed in favor of its equivalent *th*, and *þþ* also has been rendered *th*. The symbol *ȝ*, which has several values, has been removed in favor of *y, gh,* or *h*, as linguistic evidence has seemed to warrant. The combination *yy*, resulting from initial *ȝy*, has been written *yi*, while the combinations *ghh* and *ghth* have been written *gh* and *gth*, and *hh* before a consonant has been written *h*. Compound prepositions and adverbs are joined or separated according to present-day English custom whenever the context has allowed. The first person singular of the personal pronoun, when it stands alone, has been capitalized and written *I* instead of the scribal *y* which frequently represents it. In all other matters, the scribal spelling has been preserved.

Certain aspects of the manuscripts have required special consideration. Passages too badly damaged to be read except on the basis of editorial conjecture have been eliminated and replaced by brief prose summaries. Marginal signs resembling paragraph marks are often erratic, and for this reason they have been ignored. Also ignored are decorated capital letters which sometimes occur without any apparent significance and which may have been purely ornamental in purpose. In addition, I have disregarded incipits, explicits, and amens, except where they affect the meaning of a particular passage; pairs of small parallel lines appearing erratically before some lines of verse; and brackets connecting rhyme words in some of the poems. In *The South English Legendary*, however, it has seemed necessary to preserve the *punctus elevatus* which divides the lines of verse in most manuscripts, since it may have had some metrical significance not related to the punctuation. (The *punctus elevatus* is represented by a raised period.) There has been no attempt to repair faulty rhymes or to give precise accounts of the dialect in fifteenth-century materials. Only in cases where the manuscript reading fails to make sense have I made use of editorial emendation. The arrangement of lines of verse into stanzas is in three cases editorial: "The Clerk Who Would See Our Lady," "Theophilus," and "The Good Knight and His Jealous Wife."

Most of the items here represented are extant in unique manuscripts. In the case of *The South English Legendary* and *The North English Homily Collection*, there are too many manuscripts and too many differences in dialect among them to make possible, in a project of this size and purpose, a study of the variant readings. However, the fact that Hoccleve's miracle of the Virgin has been edited from a manuscript thought to be in the poet's own hand gives some importance to the variant readings in the other manuscripts containing his poem, and they have been duly recorded except for minute differences in form and in spelling. Following this precedent, variant readings have been noted for Lydgate's "The Legend of Dan Joos."

With regard to the glossary, the problem of defining words in a variety of dialects and in compositions widely separated in time has argued in favor of footnote annotation. Common Middle English words likely to be familiar to anyone who has had a first course in Chaucer are not glossed unless there is some particular difficulty involved. Also excluded are words found in present-day English with essentially the same form and meaning, and words which the context renders obvious. Each story is glossed separately, but words are not repeated within the same one unless there is a special reason for doing so. The glossary has been compiled on the basis of *The Oxford English Dictionary* and of those fascicles of the *Middle English Dictionary* (ed. Hans Kurath, Ann Arbor, Michigan) which have been issued up to the present time. For special difficulties involving Northern dialect, *Jamieson's Dictionary of the Scottish Language* (Edinburgh, 1895) has been very useful. In dealing with *The South English Legendary* I have found much valuable information in the glossary of the edition of this legendary recently published by Charlotte D'Evelyn and Anna J. Mill (Early English Text Society, Original Series, No. 244 [London, 1959], pp. 40-82). Along with these lexicons, the glossary in Professor Robinson's 1957 edition of Chaucer's works has been invaluable.

It would be impossible to express the full extent of my gratitude to those who have given so generously of their time and advice to help me in the preparation of this volume. Several of the poems here presented were originally included in a doctoral dissertation submitted in 1955 to the Faculty of Philosophy, Columbia University, under the direction of Professors Roger S. Loomis and Elliott V. K. Dobbie. Since no student can adequately thank his teachers for the gift of time and training, I can only hope that this book will prove useful enough to justify their interest and encouragement. In making this acknowledgment, I also wish to express my indebtedness, and my thanks, to the late Laura H. Loomis, whose fine scholarship has been an inspiration to me and whose friendship I shall never forget.

For the idea of presenting the miracles of the Virgin in the form of an anthology of representative tales, I am indebted to Professor Bertram Colgrave, emeritus of the University of Durham, and I am very grateful to Professor Dobbie for numerous suggestions concerning the glosses. I must also acknowledge my appreciation of some suggestions concerning the scribal spelling which Professor Robinson has made. To Professor M. M. Crow, of the University of Texas, I am indebted for his examination of the first draft of this project and for comments which have been helpful in the process of revision. I am also grateful to Professor R. W. Southern, of Balliol College, Oxford, for discussing with me his investigations of Mussafia's studies of the miracles of the Virgin before his findings appeared in print. To Herbert C. Schulz, of the Henry E. Huntington Library, I am grateful for much advice in dealing with the mysteries of paleography.

The librarians of the British Museum, the Bodleian Library, the Lincoln Cathedral Chapter Library, and the Huntington Library have been very generous in allowing me to examine manuscripts and rare books in their institutions. To them and to the librarians of the National Library of Scotland, the Royal College of Physicians, Edinburgh, the Lambeth Palace Library, and the colleges of Oxford and Cambridge universities, acknowledgment is here made for photostats and microfilms. Acknowledgment is also made to Columbia University for the privilege of holding a Lizette Andrews Fisher Fellowship in 1955 and to the University of Texas for a grant toward clerical assistance in 1957. Last of all, though only in point of time, I wish to express my sincere appreciation of the research grant made to me in the summer of 1960 by the trustees of the Henry E. Huntington Library and Art Gallery and my admiration of the Huntington staff, who have not only been most helpful to me in my work, but who have also made their library a wonderful place in which to work.

BEVERLY BOYD

San Marino, California
September 1960

CONTENTS

CONTENTS

ILLUSTRATIONS

From engravings made by John Carter in 1784 and 1785 of paintings in St. Mary's Chapel of Winchester Cathedral, Hampshire. The series of engravings is found in John Carter's *Specimens of the Ancient Sculpture and Painting Now Remaining in This Kingdom*, London, 1780-[1794].

THE MIDDLE ENGLISH MIRACLES

OF THE VIRGIN

INTRODUCTION

MIRACLES of the Virgin are tales of wonders attributed to Mary's intercession. Since they are folklore, nothing really definite is known about their origin except that they arose in the eastern Mediterranean region. Many deal with themes characteristic of that area: acts of early saints and patriarchs, deeds of emperors, conversions among pagans and Jews, and cures worked by images capable even of coming to life. A fairly large number have come down to us in Middle English, and the fame of Chaucer's "Prioress's Tale" more than justifies a quest for them. The result of this quest is an impressive collection of fanciful tales, including one by Hoccleve and one by Lydgate.

The term "fanciful" is used advisedly, for these are legends in the modern sense as well as in the technical sense that classifies them as hagiography. Rarely do we find proof that people regarded any of them as factual. Their presence in our literature is partly a result of the tendency of folklore to migrate. When this agglomeration of stories began to drift into western Europe, there developed along with the older ones tales of local origin. The *Libri miraculorum* of Gregory of Tours (ca. 538–ca. 594) are the earliest writings in the West which contain miracles of the Virgin.[1]

Stories of Our Lady's miracles must have been carried into Britain by about the same time, for examples can be found in the works of Adamnan of Iona (ca. 624–704).[2] Later on both Bede (ca. 672–735)[3] and Aelfric (ca. 955–ca. 1020)[4] employed them in religious writings, to illustrate an incident in the life of a holy person or to point a moral. It was probably in connection with such purposes as these, particularly as applied to the writing and preaching of sermons, that whole collections of miracles of the Virgin, often

[1] In Jacques Paul Migne, *Patrologiae cursus completus*, Series Latina, Vol. LXXI (Paris, 1879), cols. 713-716.

[2] "De locis sanctis," in Migne, *Patrologiae*, Ser. Latina, Vol. LXXXVIII (1862), cols. 813-814.

[3] "De Sancta Maria Virgine," in Migne, *Patrologiae*, Ser. Latina, Vol. XCIV (1862), cols. 422-423.

[4] "De assumptione beate Mariae," in *The Homilies of the Anglo-Saxon Church*, Part I, *Sermones catholici*, ed. Benjamin Thorpe (London, 1844), p. 448.

called *mariales*, came into being. The titles of some suggest that they were used as source books of *exempla* or sermon anecdotes.

A few of these *mariales* are astonishingly large, and they are valuable to us for that reason, preserving as they do a tremendous quantity of medieval narrative. But this circumstance, while admittedly interesting, is inclined to be deceptive. An objective consideration of their contents reveals for the most part commonplace writing, generally so brief as to be uncharacteristic of its time. If we are looking for narrative art and for real poetry, we shall find little of the sort here, and much of the scholarship that has been lavished upon the *mariales* is not justified by their literary merit. As source books, however, and as records of medieval legends, their fame rests unchallenged, and as such it is important to know something about them even though we must look elsewhere for the best literary examples of miracles of the Virgin.

Among the earliest extant *mariales* are those containing the local legends of places in France where there were shrines and cathedrals of Our Lady. Chartres, Laon, Coutances, Soissons, Roc-Amadour, and Saint-Pierre-sur-Dives had their own collections of miracles of the Virgin, probably compiled by members of the clergy.[5] But far more numerous are the collections of a more varied nature, made up from the common stock of materials that have been described, and a great deal of attention has been given to the discovery of the original *mariales* of this type. These were identified by Adolfo Mussafia in 1886 as a result of his comparative study of all the collections of miracles of the Virgin then known. Mussafia observed that most collections contain three nuclei of similar tales. He had to name these three groups of tales in order to talk about them, so he called two of them by the initials of their first and last members according to the titles he had devised for them in his own language (German): *HM* (for "Hildefonsus"–"Murieldis") and *TS* (for "Toledo"–"Samstag"). These groups he ascribed to the eleventh century and the twelfth century, respectively. The third group, which he called *Die Elemente* (*The Elements*) because its stories seemed to him associated with earth, air, fire, and water, he attributed to the eleventh century. Ever since their publi-

---

[5] For references to editions, see Evelyn Faye Wilson, ed. *The Stella maris of John of Garland* (Cambridge, Mass., 1946), p. 4.

4

"How Our Lady Restored a Scribe's Hand"

"The Woman Who Stole Our Lady's Child"

"How Our Lady Completed a Chapel"

"The Drowned Sacristan"

cation, Mussafia's studies of *mariales* and the legends they contain have been considered the authoritative work on the miracles of the Virgin.[6]

Mussafia's findings, however, rest on a series of highly complicated manuscript interrelationships. They are so involved that the reader is left with the impression that Mussafia did not understand them himself. Many subsequent discussions of the miracles of the Virgin have merely described his classification of the legends without additional comment, and the adoption of his system of nomenclature (which would have been more appropriate for a genre embracing materials written in many languages if he had devised it in Latin) is now so universal that it cannot be abandoned without confusion. In fact, so rigorously has his terminology been preserved that some of the tales have acquired English titles literally translated from the German, with such absurdity as "The Jew Boy" for Mussafia's "Der Judenknabe."

A badly needed re-examination of Mussafia's research has been carried out successfully by R. W. Southern, who, by giving closer attention to some important English manuscripts which Mussafia did not personally examine, has been able to provide much more concrete information about the early *mariales* and the stories found in them. In his article "The English Origins of the 'Miracles of the Virgin' "[7] he has demonstrated on the basis of internal evidence that *HM* and *TS* originated as one work, from the hand of Anselm the Younger, nephew of the famous Archbishop of Canterbury of that name, and also prior of Bury St. Edmunds. In addition to this, he has shown that the *Elements* series was originally a collection of fourteen tales and that it was the work of Dominic, prior of Evesham. If Southern is right, and there is little doubt that he is, both works belong to the early twelfth century, and both are in origin English and monastic.

The works of Anselm and of Dominic must have been very widely read both in England and on the Continent, for many later *mariales* are directly or indirectly related to them. In the

---

[6] "Studien zu den mittelalterlichen Marienlegenden," *Sitzungsberichte der kaiserlichen Akademie der Wissenschaften in Wien, Phil.-hist. Klasse*, CXIII (1886), 917-994; CXV (1887), 5-92; CXIX (1889), Fasc. ix; CXXIII (1890), Fasc. viii; CXXXIX (1898), Fasc. viii.

[7] *Mediaeval and Renaissance Studies*, IV (1958), 176-216.

introduction to her edition of the *Stella maris* of Johannes de Garlandia (whom she calls John of Garland), Evelyn Faye Wilson has included a genealogy (facing p. 76) of such works. Here may be found important and famous *mariales* by Gautier de Coincy (1177–1236)[8] and Caesarius von Heisterbach (who wrote his collection of miracles of the Virgin ca. 1223–1227).[9] Wilson does not mention Alfonso X (King of Castile and León, 1252–1284), whose *Cantigas de Santa Maria* are of interest to students of both music and literature.[10] Not all collections of miracles of the Virgin occupy volumes of their own. Some are appended to other books, as in the case of the "Promptuarium discipuli de miraculis beate virginis" by Johannes Herolt (1400–1450), which is usually added to one or more of his other works in both the manuscripts and the printed editions. Also, in both the *Speculum historiale* of Vincent de Beauvais (ca. 1190–ca. 1264)[11] and the *Legenda aurea* (ca. 1255) of Jacobus de Voragine,[12] collections of miracles of the Virgin are woven into works which are not themselves *mariales*.

Many poems and plays were based on miracles of the Virgin. The story of Theophilus, who sold his soul to the Devil and was afterward saved by Our Lady, was the favorite theme of all. To list but a few literary works inspired by it, there is a version in Leonine hexameters written by Hroswitha of Gandersheim (ca. 935–ca. 1002),[13] a miracle play written between 1254 and 1285 by the trouvère Rutebeuf,[14] and a tail-rhyme romance by an anonymous English poet which has come down to us in a fifteenth-century manuscript, MS. Rawlinson Poetry 225 of the Bodleian Library, and is here edited from that source. While these and similar literary works are available in good editions, the *mariales*, probably because of their size, have attracted more interest. For example, Ruth W. Tryon has devoted sixty-five pages of an article

---

[8] *Les miracles de la Sainte Vierge*, ed. Alexandre Poquet (Paris, 1857).

[9] *Dialogus miraculorum*, ed. Joseph Strange (Cologne, 1851).

[10] Ed. Leopoldo Augusto de Cueto (Madrid, 1889).

[11] (Venice, 1494.)

[12] Ed. Theodor Graesse, 2nd ed. (Leipzig, 1850). For discussion and bibliographical references concerning the date, see Minnie E. Wells, "The *South English Legendary* in Its Relation to the *Legenda Aurea*," *PMLA*, LI (1936), 337-340.

[13] "Lapsus et conversio Theophili vicedomini," in *Hrotsvithae opera*, ed. Karl Strecker (Leipzig, 1906), pp. 67-80.

[14] *Le miracle de Théophile*, ed. Grace Frank (Paris, 1925).

on the Middle English miracles of the Virgin to collected materials, which are further emphasized by being treated first, whereas she has devoted only sixteen pages to what she calls "scattered texts": the finest pieces of their kind in English.[15]

Since the present study is particularly concerned with miracles of the Virgin written in Middle English, it is now necessary to look more closely at the genre as it developed in England after the time of Anselm and Dominic. It would appear that the next writer after them to deal with these same legends was William of Malmesbury, one of the better-known chroniclers of the twelfth century. His *mariale*, written ca. 1143, covers some of Anselm's materials and could have been intended, as Southern has suggested, to correct certain details.[16] These three collections (Anselm's, Dominic's, and that of William of Malmesbury) were afterward conflated. The resulting work came into the possession of a canon of St. Paul's named Alberic, and Alberic's book was translated into Anglo-Norman late in the twelfth century by a poet named William Adgar.[17] Adgar's *mariale* is thought to be the first one written in England in a vernacular tongue.

There must have been considerable writing of this type in Anglo-Norman in England, probably much that has been lost. After Adgar's, there is a second Anglo-Norman *mariale* from the twelfth century, though since Paul Meyer, who edited its legends,[18] hesitated to place its composition in England, the name "Second Anglo-Norman Collection" has been applied to an anonymous group of sixty miracles of the Virgin in MS. Royal B.xiv (late thirteenth or early fourteenth century) of the British Museum.[19] Of another collection, written by a monk of Bury St. Edmunds named Everard de Gateley in the second half of the thirteenth century, only three of the tales have survived. These are in MS.

---

[15] "Miracles of Our Lady in Middle English Verse," *PMLA*, XXXVIII (1923), 308-388.

[16] "The English Origins," pp. 200-201. The principal manuscript is MS. 97 (thirteenth century) of Salisbury Cathedral.

[17] Carl Neuhaus, ed. *Adgar's Marienlegenden nach der Londoner Handschrift Egerton 612*, Altfranzösische Bibliothek, No. 9 (Heilbronn, 1886).

[18] "Notice sur un manuscrit d'Orléans contenant d'anciens miracles de la Vierge en vers français," *Notices et extraits des manuscrits de la Bibliothèque Nationale et autres bibliothèques*, XXXIV, Part 2 (1895), 31-56.

[19] Hilding Kjellman, ed. *La deuxième collection anglo-normande des miracles de la Sainte Vierge et son original latin* (Paris, 1922).

Rawlinson Poetry 241 (early fourteenth century) of the Bodleian Library.[20]

The vernacular tradition in England is thus seen to be very old with regard to the miracles of the Virgin, though this does not imply that tales ceased to be written in Latin. The earliest written in Middle English have long been thought to be the ones found in manuscripts of a complicated mass of hagiographical and liturgical compositions to which scholars have given the name *The South English Legendary*. The complication arises from the fact that the manuscripts are garbled and incomplete, exhibiting much variation from one to another without any visible reason. Recent investigation has shown that *The South English Legendary* as we now have it is probably not a work in its original form but an assortment of manuscripts copied from fragments representing a lost *liber festivalis* (book of readings for the ecclesiastical year) and at least one revision of it.[21]

The oldest manuscript of *The South English Legendary*, MS. Laud 108 (ca. 1280–1290) of the Bodleian Library, contains only one miracle of the Virgin, "Theophilus" (foll. 127^b-130).[22] There was good reason to include this miracle of the Virgin in a *liber festivalis*, for Theophilus was considered a genuine saint. The whole group of miracles, including "Theophilus," first appears in the second oldest manuscript of *The South English Legendary*, MS. Harley 2,277 (ca. 1300; foll. 58-64^b) of the British Museum. The other Harley miracles (two of which are edited in the present volume) resemble "Theophilus" so closely that there can be no reasonable doubt of their common origin. Whether they were composed for *The South English Legendary* or added to it from the same source in the process of revision we do not know.

Any attempt to write a chronological history of the genre as it appeared in Middle English is complicated by the fact that "Theophilus" is found in MS. Laud 108 without the miracles of the Virgin that follow it in MS. Harley 2,277. It is further complicated by the existence of another Middle English tale, entirely different

[20] Paul Meyer, "Notice du MS. Rawlinson Poetry 241 (Oxford)," *Romania*, XXIX (1900), 1-84.

[21] See my "New Light on *The South English Legendary*," *Texas Studies in English*, XXXVII (1958), 187-194.

[22] Edited by Carl Horstmann, *The Early South-English Legendary or Lives of Saints*, EETS, Orig. Ser., No. 87 (London, 1887), pp. 288-293.

in style and structure from anything in the legendary, in MS. Digby 86 (ca. 1275; foll. 130-132) of the Bodleian Library, under the title "Coment le sauter Noustre Dame fu primes cuntrové."[23] With all due allowance for the difficulty of arriving at precise dates for manuscripts, the Digby poem may be placed at about the same time as the Laud text of "Theophilus," and it may be even older.

Collectively, these items show that writing of the kind was done in Middle English in the last quarter of the thirteenth century, if not before. How much was actually written this early is a question which cannot be answered, and it is interesting to find that the entire corpus of miracles of the Virgin now extant in Middle English is considerably smaller than those which have come down to us in Latin and in French. This is still more interesting when we remember that English men of letters were doing creative writing in the three languages as late as Gower's time.

All of the Middle English miracles of the Virgin that have any literary significance are in verse, and they follow the forms usual for narrative poetry in their day, except that there is no miracle play extant. This, however, need not mean that none was ever written, since we know that a great deal of material has been lost. The outstanding miracle of the Virgin in English, perhaps in any language, is Chaucer's "Prioress's Tale." The reason it is outstanding cannot be the story itself, for whatever Chaucer's immediate source may have been, the tale of the little clergeon exists in many versions and cannot have been novel to his intended audience. In the telling, as we should expect, the legend profits from Chaucer's style, but there is another aspect of his genius in the way this miracle of the Virgin is made to reflect, and at the same time to build up, the personality of the Prioress who is supposed to be telling it. The exact ingredients of this procedure are Chaucer's secret, but at least part of his success must reside in his fortunate choice of a liturgical frame for the story.

We might suppose that the "Prioress's Tale" had considerable influence upon the literary genre to which it belongs, but this does

---

[23] Edited by Horstmann, *Altenglische Legenden*, Neue Folge (Heilbronn, 1881), pp. 220-224. Another copy of the same poem appears in MS. Auchinleck (1330-1340; foll. 259-260b) of the National Library of Scotland and is edited by David Laing, *A Penni Worth of Witte* (Edinburgh, 1857), pp. 97-106.

not seem to have been the case at all. With due consideration of the possibility that materials now lost once contained indebtedness to Chaucer, the only extant miracles of the Virgin which show his influence are those of Thomas Hoccleve (ca. 1368–ca. 1437) and John Lydgate (ca. 1370–ca. 1450), both of which are edited in this volume. Even here, the indebtedness is general, unless specific imitation be seen in the fact that both poems are written, like Chaucer's, in rhyme royal.

In England, the miracles of the Virgin did not long survive the fifteenth century as an active literary genre. This was largely part of a trend of the times, since hagiography went into a decline. Eventually Protestantism ended their popularity in England. The last English miracle of the Virgin known to scholars at the present time is a version of "Theophilus" written ca. 1572 by William Forrest, chaplain to Queen Mary I.[24]

This survey of the Middle English miracles of the Virgin therefore begins at the close of the thirteenth century and ends at the close of the Middle Ages. The character of the materials is exactly what we might expect: international rather than English and popular rather than learned. Their anti-Semitism is the heritage of centuries of bigotry and persecution throughout the world. Their morality is entirely theological, and there are many things about the tales which lessen their appeal in an age that does not admire the blind faith they extol. Taken together, the tales are an interesting cross section of medieval thought, culture, and narrative traditions. Above all, the miracles of the Virgin are valuable to us because they were widely familiar to medieval writers and to the people for whom their works were intended.

---

[24] Edited by Franz Ludorff, "William Forrest's Theophuslegende," *Anglia*, VII (1884), 81-113.

How Our Lady Came to the Devil
Instead of the Victim

Foll. 61ᵇ-63

A knight was while a riche man   ·   that honurede moche mid alle
Oure Levedi and alle hire festes   ·   that in the yer doth falle.
A gret feste he huld upe his poer   ·   everech of hire daye
And fondede to honure   ·   oure suete Levedy and paye.
5 Sithe hit biful as God hit wolde   ·   that his god him was bynome,
That he ne mighte noght holde up his honur   ·   so pore he was bicome.
In grete meseise he ladde his lyf   ·   and yut him grevede more
That he ne mighte do as he dude er   ·   and aschamed was ful sore.
Whan hit com to Oure Levedi Dai   ·   that he moste his feste holde,
10 He ne mighte for schame among men beo   ·   so lute of him me tolde.
O tyme ayen Oure Levedi Day   ·   as scholde his feste beo,
To wode he wende and hudde him   ·   that me ne scholde him noght iseo.
The Devel com in a manes forme   ·   to him wel sone there
And axede such man as he was   ·   whi he theron so were.
15 "Nai, certes," quath this knight,   ·   "mi manhode is al forlore;
For schame that ich was while man   ·   ich hude me her therfore."
"Riche man ich wole the maki sone,"   ·   the Devel aye sede,
"Of wordles catel and murgthe ynough   ·   if thu dost bi mi rede."

4 *MS indicates a second* punctus elevatus *after* Levedy.

1 while] once   mid alle] withal   3 huld] held   poer] power; upe his poer:
as well as he could   4 fondede] tried   paye] please   5 Sithe] Afterward
god] property   bynome] taken away   6 holde up his honur] maintain his
dignity(?)   7 meseise] poverty   9 that] when   moste] must   10 me]
indefinite pronoun; so lute of him me tolde: people held him in so slight regard;
cf. line 12   11 O] One   ayen] toward   as] when   12 To wode] To a wood
hudde him] hid himself   14 whi he theron so were] why he was in there in that
manner   17 aye sede] replied   18 wordles catel] worldly goods   murgthe]
pleasure   if thu dost bi mi rede] if you take my advice

"Leove Sire," quath this seli knight, · "sai what ich schal do
20 To bringe me out of thisse meseise · and ich wole don also."
"Bote go hom," quath this lithere wight, · "and god ynough thu schalt fynde,
And com hider to me thulke day · and ne bilef noght thi wyf bihynde,
Ac bring hire and we schole · of sum foreward speke,
That thu schalt evere riche beo · bote thu thi foreward breke."
25 Tho was this a god womman · and lovede wel Seinte Marie,
Therfore the Devel hire wolde habbe · for he hadde therto envie.
The Devel wende forth his wey; · the knight hamward drough.
Tho he com hom, in eche hurne · he fond god ynough.
Yurne he thonkede the foule wight · that yaf him such cas,
30 Him lange and him eschte sone · ac he nuste what he was.
That hit was atte daye · that hi bituene hem nome,
His wyf he het greithi hire · that heo with him come.
He nolde nothing hire telle · whider he wolde fare;
Hi wende bothe toward the wode · tho hi were yare.
35 Bi a chapel of Oure Levedi · bi the wey hi come ride.
The levedi bad heo moste alighte · and a stounde abide
To bidde hire bedes to Oure Levedi · as heo was iwoned ofte;
Tho heo into the chapel com · he ful adoun aslepe softe.
Oure Levedi suete and mylde · alighte fram Hevene to hire there,
40 Hire forme in eche poynte · hireselve as thegh hit were.
With the knight as his owe wyf · heo wende wyth him and rod;
The knight bigan to chide faste · that heo so longe abod.
"Sire, Sire," quath Oure Levedi, · "we ne beoth noght longe ilet;
Ous ne schal for oure abode · spede bote the bet.
45 Ich hopie thin erande · schal beo wel ibet."
Forth hi wende into the wode · ther the stede was iset.
Tho hi come toward the stede · the Devel was yare bifore;

---

33 whider, *MS blurred at* i.   35 *MS repeats* hi come.

19 Leove] Dear   seli] miserable   21 lithere wight]
evil creature   22 thulke day] on the appointed
day   bilef] leave   23 Ac] But   foreward] agreement   25 Tho] Since
26 envie] desire   28 Tho] When   hurne] corner   29 Yurne] Eagerly   he
thonkede] *context seems to require* he would thank.   30 He longed [to find him]
and would have asked about him at once, but he did not know who he was
31 When it was the day they had agreed upon   32 He told his wife to get
dressed, that she might come with him   33 nothing] at all   fare] journey
34 Hi] They   yare] ready   35 bi the wey hi come ride] they came riding along
the way; come *is past tense plural*, ride *a dependent infinitive.*   36 stounde] time
37 To bidde hire bedes] To say her prayers   iwoned] accustomed   38 he] she;
cf. line 71   41 owe] own   43 ilet] delayed   44 It shall but go the better
with us for our delay(?)   45 ibet] made good   47 yare] ready, *or perhaps an
error for* thare

12

Ac tho [the] Devel Oure Levedi isegh · he gan to grede sore.
"Fale trattour!" he seide to the knight, · "whi bitrayestou me so?
50 Schal ich habbe this for mi godhede · that ich habbe the ido?"
"Ne holde ich the foreward?" quath the knight; · "wharof dostou mene?"
"Thu lixt loude," quath the Devel; · "thu breghst forward al clene:
Thu bringst with the mi meste fo · and scholdest with the thi wyf lede."
This knight hovede al witles; · he nuste hou he sede.
55 "Thu lithere thing!" quath Oure Levedi; · "whi woldestou so fawe
That he hadde his wyf ibroght? · thu wost hit nere no lawe."
"Ich wole the sigge," quath the schrewe; · "heo is me suythe loth:
For heo him serveth so wel · he maketh me alday wroth.
And if heo havede hider icome · ich hire wolde astrangli anon,
60 Ac thu ert evere mi worste freond · among alle mi fon.
Thu hire hast nou bynome me; · thu bringst me al to grounde.
Allas that thu evere were; · allas thulke stounde!"
"Ich hote the," quath Oure Levedi, · "ich hote the hunne wende,
That thu negh this man ne come · nevere for to schende.
65 And thu, Sire Knight, also god, · thu me hast igremed sore;
Beo repentant of thi trespas; · ne do thu so no more.
Al that thu hast of richesce · thurf the Develes sonde
Del hit al for Godes love · povere men in the londe,
And thu schalt habbe yut god ynough · to lede bi thi lyf;
70 In mi chapel ther thu wost · thu schalt fynde thi wyf."
Mid this word he wende forth; · the knight ne segh hire no more.
He understod wel ho hit was; · he gan to sike sore
For the sinne that he dude · thurf the Fundes lore.
Oure Levedi he bad foryevenisse · and cride hire milce and ore.
75 Hamward he wende in gret thoght; · his wyf slepinge he fonde
In the chapel ther heo lay · slepinge al thulke stounde.
Slepinge heo hadde al iseye · of hem al hou hit was;
Gret joye hi makeden hem bituene · as hi tolde of this cas.
Faire hi wende togadere hom · and dude Oure Levedi bone,
80 And that hi hadde thurf the Devel · pore men hi delde sone,

48 grede] cry out   49 Fale] False(?); *probably an error for* Fals
50 godhede] goodness   51 mene] complain   52 Thu lixt loude] You
are lying aloud   thu breghst forward al clene] you completely break the agreement
53 meste] greatest   54 hovede] stood there   55 fawe] eagerly   56 lawe]
justice   57 sigge] say   suythe] very   61 bynome] taken away   63 hote]
command   hunne] hence   64 negh] near   65 igremed] angered   67 thurf]
through   sonde] sending   68 Del] Distribute   69 to lede bi thi lyf] to live on
71 segh] saw   72 sike] sigh   73 Fundes] Fiend's   74 milce] mercy
ore] grace   76 ther] where   79 bone] request

And servede Oure Levede wel · that hem was mylde and hende,
And wordles god hadde ynough · to here lyves ende.
Of Oure Levedi faire miracles · we seoth al day and grete;
Thegh we habbe of summe itold · yut nole we noght lete.

81 hende] gracious   82 here] their   84 lete] stop

The Oxford Scholars

Foll. 63-64

A knight ther was in Engelond · by northe her biside;
A yung child he hadde bi his wyf · as God wolde hit scholde bitide.
The moder a dai while hit was yung · to churche hit broghte;
The child bihuld the rode in churche · and stod in grete thoghte.

5 "Moder," he seide, "what is the man · that yund anhongod is?"
"Sone," quath the levedi, · "hit is Oure Loverd, iwis.
For ous he was so anhonge · and to dethe ibroght;
To bringe ous to the joye of Hevene · he hath ous deore iboght."
"Wel aughte we thanne," quath the child, · "servi him with wille;

10 And what is thulke faire womman · that stent bi him so stille?"
"Hit is his moder," quath the levedi, · "that oure suete Levedi is."
"Ou, madame," quath the child, · "wounder me thingth hit, iwis.
Stod heo bi him tho me him slough?" · The levedi seide, "Ye."
"Awey, madame," quath this child, · "mightestou so bi me!

15 Hou mighte heo iseo quelle hire child · that hire hurte ne brac atuo?"
"Moche del was on hire hurte · and sorinysche also."
Thegh this child were yung · of this deol ofte sithe hit thoghte;
Selthe wher he evere were · out of his hurte he hit broughte.
This child was sithe ido to scole; · hit lurnede wel ynough

20 So that he com to Oxenford · tho he to manne drough.
Selthe hit com out of his thoght · what so he iseye
The deol that Oure Levedi hadde · tho heo isegh hire sone deye.
Hit biful sithe in a tyme · as hit doth bi meni on
That he dude a dedlich synne; · so ne dude he nevere non.

25 He nolde noght as meni on wolleth · ligge theron longe:

---

6 hit, *written over a* punctus elevatus. *The scribe has placed the* punctus elevatus
after is, *probably in error since the second position interrupts the sense as well as the
meter. The scribe of the later copy of the same poem in MS. 145 (fol. 88ᵇ) of Corpus
Christi College, Cambridge, uses the first position, the one followed in the present
edition.* 15 MS *repeats* mighte *after* heo, *struck out by the scribe.* 25 ligge,
second g blurred.

---

2 bitide] happen   3 a] one   5 yund] yonder   anhongod] hanged
8 deore] dearly   10 stent] stands   12 Ou] Oh   me thingth hit] it seems to me
13 heo] she   me] *indefinite pronoun*; tho me him slough: when people slew him
14 Awey] Alas   15 quelle] kill; Hou mighte heo iseo quelle hire child: How
could she see her child killed   hurte] heart   atuo] in two   16 del] sorrow; *cf.*
line 17, deol   sorinysche] distress   17 ofte sithe] often   18 Selthe] Seldom;
a form of selde   19 ido] sent   20 to manne] to adulthood   21 iseye] saw
23 bi meni on] to many a one   25 ligge] remain

15

To a frere he wende to schrifte · his penance to afonge.
Repentant he was ynough · of thulke lithere dede
And bisoughte him for thulke sinne · that he for him bede,
And that he bede to Oure Levedi for thulke sor · that heo hadde on hire thoght
30 Tho he segh hire sone anhonge · and in stronge dethe ibroght.
That heo yive me grace and wille, · the levedi milce and freo,
Sori ynou in hurte · for mi sinne to beo:
That he bad eke himsilf · bothe night and day
For the deol of hire sone · tho heo him ded isay.
35 He hadde the while he lyvede · thulke bone in mone
That Oure Levedi tho he was ded · him cudde and eke hire sone.
Atte laste at Oxenford · at scole he gan deye.
The furste day he was iwist, · as the maystres iseye,
Tuey clerkes that were over him · that suythe wel his freond were
40 That wiste his bodi night and day · and were next the bere:
Ech man amorwe bote hi tueye · wende hom in his ende;
"Felawe," quath on, "hit is tyme · that we the taperes tende."
"Abyd," quath th'other, "a stounde · that this maistres come;
Hit nis noght right the tapres tende · bote hi were her some."
45 As this tuey clerkes were alone · adoun hi lynede stille,
So that hi worthe aslepe · as hit was Godes wille.
As hi slepe hem thoghte bothe · that hi angles menie iseye
Here felawes soule that ther lai ded · to Hevene lede heye.
Oure Levede as to teche the wey · hiresilve yeode bifore
50 And openede the dore of Hevene · that the soule were in ibore.
Tho heo tofore Oure Loverd com · adoun heo sat akneo;
"Sone," heo seide, "lo her mi freond · that wel hath iserved me:
Underfong him into thi joye." · Oure Loverd aye sede,
"Leove Moder, ich aughte wel · thegh thu nevere ne bede,
55 For an urthe he bad mi milce ofte · for the deol that thu iseye,

48 felawes, *first e blurred.*

---

26 afonge] receive   27 lithere] wicked   28 bede] should pray   29 sor] sorrow   on]
in   31 milce] mild(?); *probably an error for* milde   freo] generous   34 isay] saw
35 bone] request   mone] remembrance   36 tho] when   cudde] might
recognize   38 iwist] watched, *referring to the custom of keeping vigil over the
dead before burial*   39 that suythe wel his freond were] who were very good
friends of his   41 hi tueye] they two   in his ende] at his appointed time(?)
42 tende] should light   43 stounde] time   44 some] together(?); *perhaps a
form of* isamen   45 lynede] leaned   46 worthe aslepe] fell asleep   47 hem
thoghte] it seemed to them   48 heye] on high   49 teche] point out   yeode]
went   50 were] might be   51 akneo] on her knee   53 Underfong] Receive
aye sede] replied   54 bede] asked   55 an] on   milce] mercy

And that sor in thin hurte · tho thu me seye deye.
Wel fawe ich him wole afonge · as right is that ich do,
And among myn halewen him onury · and thu schalt also."
Tho sende Oure Levedi fram Hevene · to the tapres light anon,
60 That aboute the bodi stode · and tende hem echon.
The clerkes awoke anon · as hi slepe bothe ther
And fonde the tapres alle itend · as hem thoghte in slepe er.
Tho come the maistres as right was · the servise for to do,
And tho hit was to ende ibrought · and the bodi ibured also
65 The clerkes to here prive maistre · tolde al that hi seye
That Oure Levedi to Oure Loverd seide · in the joye of Hevene heye,
And hou hi onurede him for the munde · that he hadde her in mode
Of the deol that Oure Levedi hadde · of hire sone in the rode.
Hi yeode forth to the frere · that his schrift-fader was,
70 Somme of the maistres priveiliche · and tolde him of that cas.
The frere seide that hit was soth · that he hadde er in mode
The deol that Oure Levedi hadde · tho hire sone deide on the rode.
The miracle was tho iholde soth · of this holi childe.
With eche thing alday we seoth · Oure Levedi suete and mylde.

57 fawe] eagerly   58 halewen] saints   onury] honor   65 seye] saw
67 munde] remembrance   mode] mind   68 in the rode] on the cross

MS. Ch.5.21 (fourteenth century),
Royal College of Physicians, Edinburgh

The Pilgrim of St. James

Foll. 23^b-24

Emendations (bracketed) are from John Small's
edition, in his *English Metrical Homilies from
Manuscripts of the Fourteenth Century* (Edinburgh, 1862), pp. 53-59.

Twas a man, als ic herd say,
That til Sain Jamis hit the way,
And that day that he suld wend
He mad a fest til al his frend.
5 Fel auntour that he was sa gladde
That Satenas mad him ful madde,
And gert him dedeli sinne
Wit a womman that was tharinne.
Quen he havid his sin don,
10 Apon his way he went him son,
And he that gert him falle in blam
Met him in liknes of Sain Jam
And askid him quider he wald wende.
Bot he wist noht it was the Fende,
15 And said, "I mac mi vaiage
Til Sain Jam in pilgrimage."
The Fend ansuerd and said sone,

2 til] to   hit] took   3 suld] should   5 Fel
auntour] It happened   7 gert] caused   9 Quen]
When   15 vaiage] journey

"No wat thou noht quat thou havis done
In licheri igaines me?

20 It es Sain [Jam] that spekis wit the.
Thou ert unworthi me to seke.
Thi vayage es noht worthe a leke.
Wend thou thi sin fra me to hide?
Quen thou it did I was biside.

25 Thi vaiage may noht pai me
Bot ef thou do that I bid the."
This man wend that he Sain Jam ware,
And said, "Laverd, ic am al yare
For [to] be boxom you to,

30 And do al that ye sai me to."
"Ga swithe," he said, "and geld the,
That I thi repentanze mai se,
And scher thi thort in tua riht son:
For havis thou mi wille don,

35 And quen thou havis theselvin slan,
Til Hevin salle I ger the be tane."
This pilgrim wend to pai Sain Jam,
And did himselvin mikel scham,
And he schar al awai ful rathe

40 His members and his penndanz bathe,
And sithen he schar his throt in tua.
And son quen he hafede don sua,
Satanas was ful redie,
And tok that sawel gredilye,

45 And mad ful gret joi of his prai,
And tilward Helle he tok the wai.
Sain Peter and Sain Jam him mette,
And bathe thai gan his wai to lette,
And Sain Jam said to the Fend,

50 "Quider wilto wit mi pilgrim wend?"
And he ansuerd and said, "Til Helle,
Thar he sal for his sinnis duel.

23 Wend thou] Did you think
25 pai] please   28 yare] ready
29 boxom] obedient   31 swithe] quickly
33 thort] throat   36 ger the be tane] cause you
to be taken   37 wend] thought   39 rathe]
quickly   46 tilward] toward   48 lette] hinder
52 Thar] Where

For he was his awen ban,
Forthi in him part haf ye nan.

55 Wit riht and resoun he es mine,
To wend wit me til Helle pine."
Than ansuerd Sain Jam for his man,
And said, "Thou lies, traytour Satan.
Thou wat wel, Thef, thou havis the woh,

60 For in my nam himself he sloh.
He wend wel that thou havid ben I
Quen thou gert him do his folye.
In deed was he til me bowxom,
And forthi sal he wit me com."

65 The Fend said, "That mai noht be.
Wit riht and law mai thou se
That he es min thoru jogement,
For quen he on his vayage went
He filed his sawel dedelye

70 Wit the filth of licherye,
And sithen wit his awen knife
He set himselvin of his life.
Wy, sai me Jam, on quatkin wisse
Moht he mar dey in mi servise?

75 Loc quether I wit riht and lawe
May him wit me til Helle drawe."
Sain Jam ansuerd and said him to,
"Wrang no wille I nan the do.
Bot yef we wil the sothe treye,

80 Gon we til dom of Our Levedye,
And als scho demes sal it be,
For that es riht als think me."
And Sain Peter, his felawe,

61 *MS repeats* wend.

---

53 ban] murderer   54 Forthi]
For that reason   56 pine] pain   59 thou
havis the woh] you are in the wrong   66 law]
justice   69 filed] defiled   72 set] laid violent
hands upon; He set himselvin of his life: He
committed suicide   73 quatkin] what kind; on
quatkin wisse: in what manner   74 dey] die
79 treye] assay   80 dom] judgment
81 demes] judges   82 als think me] as it seems
to me

Said, "This think me [riht] and lawe.
85 Mari," he said, "es god justise.
Scho wil do wrang on nane wyse."
Quen thai com bifor Ur Levedye,
Scho demid son wit hir mercye
At that sawel til the bodie
90 Suld turn and penance do worthi,
And said, "This sawel, als it nou isse,
Mai nangat cum til Hevin blis
Ar it be clensed in bodye
Of sin wit penanze worthi.

95 Forthi for jugement gif I
That it turn til the bodye
And clens it wit [worthi] penanze
And yem it sithen fra meschanze."
The Fend for this dom was sarie
100 And ille payed that Our Levedye
Havid reft him wit riht jogement
That man that he wit gil had schent.
Quen this sawel was cumen igain
To the bodi, this man was fain
105 And monc in Cluny he him yald,
And tis tal til his abbot tald,
Hou he was schent thoru gilri
And saved thoru Our Levedi.
Georard he hiht, and fra that tim
110 That Satenas hafd gabbed him
Hali man he was and god,
And servid Godd wit miht and mod,
Bot thar his throt was scorn wit knif
A red merk was al his lif,
115 And thar his membres was bifore
Havid he noht sithen bot a bore.
Bi this tale har may we se
That wis and wair bihoves us be

89 At] That   90 turn] return
92 nangat] in no wise   93 Ar] Before
98 yem] keep   99 sarie] distressed   104 fain]
glad   107 gilri] guile   110 gabbed] deceived
112 mod] mind   113 thar] where   scorn] cut
117 har] here   118 wair] cautious

That Satenas ne ger us rayk
120 Fra rihtwisnes to sinful laik,
For yef he find us out of stret
He bindes us bathe hand and fete.
That es at say, ef he us find
In dedeli sin he may us bind
125 Wit wik will and ger us wend
Fra sin to sin and sua us schend.
For, als he gert this pilgrim ga
Fra sin to sin and himself sla,
Sua gers he man ga gastilye
130 Fra glotouny to licherye,
Fra lychery to covaytye,
And sua to prid and envye,
And at the last in his prisoun
He dos him, als thef in prisoun,
135 Quen he gers him in wanhop falle,
For wanhop his prisoun I calle.
For quasa cumes anes tharinne
Tharof may he noht lihtli winne,
For qua deyes in that prisoun
140 His sawel es broht til a donjoun
Thar it witouten end sal lend
Wit al faas, witouten frend,
For it bes felaw wit the Fend
That snellik sal it scham and schend.
145 And quen this werd bes broht til end,
Than sal the bodi thider wend,
Wit that sari sawel to lend
Thar wormes sal it rewli rend;
Thar sal it bi that sari sinne
150 That it no wald noht hir blinne:
That soru mai na tung telle

119 Satenas, *MS has* Satenans.

---

119 rayk] wander
120 laik] sport 121 out of stret]
astray 123 at] to 125 wik] wicked
129 gastilye] in spirit 134 dos] puts
135 wanhop] despair 137 anes] once
141 lend] dwell 142 faas] foes 144 snellik]
severely 145 werd] world 148 Thar] Where
rewli] pitifully 150 hir] here blinne] stop

That it sal drey wit fendes felle.
Hald we us forthi in stret
That Satenas may us noht met,
155 That es at sai, in rihtwisnes,
Quarof Sain Jon in wildernes
Spac and bad us graythe that way
That ledis man til gamin and play.
Our Laverd in this wai us lede
160 Til Hevin and yeld us thar our med.

152 drey] endure   felle] cruel   155 That es at
sai] That is to say   157 graythe] put in order
158 gamin] sport

The Clerk Who Would See Our Lady

Foll. 37^b-38^b

[A clerk loved Our Lady so much that he prayed
fervently to behold her in a vision. An angel appeared to him, warning that he would have to pay
for such a vision with either his eyesight or his life.
The clerk accepted the conditions but hoped to
escape blindness by keeping one eye closed. The
angel returned to Heaven and came back again
as follows:]

45   Fram Heven into the clerkes bour,
     Right doun biforn his beddes fet,
     The angel alight with gret honour,
     And wel fair he gan him gret:
     "Mari, that bar our saveour,"
50   He seyd, "thou schalt sen as sket."
     With him ther com a gret odour;
     Nas never no smel half so swete:
     So swete a smal nas never non
     Of rose no of no spicerie
55   As com into that leveli won
     Bifor that leveliche compeynie.

     With angel song and miri play
     Our Levedi adoun sche light
     Into the chaumber ther he lay,

45 bour] bed chamber   50 as sket] at once
55 leveli] pleasant   won] dwelling   59 ther]
where

60 And seyd, "Clerk, drede the nowight."
Thei a man bithought him ay
No schuld he reden apo[n] aright
Hennes unto domesday
Hou fair sche is, that maiden bright:
65 Hou bright sche is no tong may telle,
Yblisced mot hye ever ben!
Of Heven, of erthe, and of Helle
Sche is emperice and quene.

A mantel Our Levedy unfeld,
70 Brighter than sonne that schineth schire.
"Clerk, drede the nought but be nou beld,
For thou schalt have thi desire.
Therwhiles thou hast thine eiyen in weld
Avise the wele of min atire.
75 Apertliche thou me biheld
Bodi and face, brest and swire."
Swire and al hir bodi he seiye
When sche hadde to him spoken.
He loked on hir with his on eiye:
80 That other he held stille yloken.

Oyain to Heven Our Levedi went,
Wel stillelich out of that clos.
The clerk held him foulely schent
Amorwe when that he aros.
85 His yalu here he hath al torent
And in his hert sore him agros.
Al thus he seyd and him biment:
"This night I saved on of mi fos—
Mi fo I spard, allas that while!

62 apo[n], *MS has* apom.

---

60 nowight] in no way   61 Thei]
Though   62 reden apo[n] aright] describe
correctly   66 hye] she   69 unfeld] unfolded
70 schire] brightly   71 beld] bold   73 Ther-
whiles] While   in weld] in possession   74 Avise
the wele of] Observe well   75 Apertliche] Openly
76 swire] neck   79 his on eiye] his one eye
81 Oyain] Again   82 clos] enclosed place
85 here] hair   torent] torn apart   86 him agros]
he shuddered to himself   87 biment] bemoaned

25

90 Sori icham, and wele ich owe;
　Min eiye doth mi soule gile
　And often bringeth it ful lowe."

　Right in his chaumber ther he stode
　Him thought his liif was him ful loth.
95 He wepe sore with dreri mode
　And out of his chaumber he goth.
　"That me no deined ich was wode
　To loke with min eiyen bothe
　Opon that levedi fair and gode.
100 I wot, therfore, that sche is wroth:
　Wroth sche is, and wele sche may,
　With me, that am sinful chaitif,
　That I schuld hir so bitraye
　That ichave loved in al mi liif.

105 Ever me may rewe that ich while
　That I schuld, for ani drede,
　Do Marie that gret gile.
　Allas, what schal me to rede?
　Mi soule I brought in gret periil.
110 A, Levedi, for thi maidenhed
　Foryive me mi sinnes vile
　And help me in this muchel nede!
　In this nede thou me save,
　That I no be never forlorn.
115 Graunt me that, I the crave,
　For his love that of the was born.

　A, Levedi, to me thou lithe;
　For care min hert wil torive.
　Michel love ichil the kithe
120 And worthschip thine joies five.
　Lene me grace another sithe
　To se thi bodi withouten strive!
　Bi so, ichil be blithe

90 owe] ought　93 ther] where　95 wepe]
wept　mode] spirit　97 I was mad not to
condescend　102 chaitif] wretch　105 ich
while] at any time　108 Alas, what counsel shall
I have　117 lithe] shelter　118 torive] break
119 kithe] show　120 worthschip] honor
121 sithe] time　122 strive] dispute

26

To be blinde in al mi live:
125 In al mi live ichil be glad
In swiche penaunce for to ben,
Bi so thou graunt that I the bad—
Efsones I mot the sen."

Alday he was in sorwe strong,
130 And afterward that com the night
His white honden hard he wrong;
He ne may for wo slepe nowight.
He herd than a miri song
Of angels that were so bright.
135 Our Levedi com hem among
And seyd, "Clerk, drede nowight!"
Sche spac the clerk so fair untille:
"Ich foryive the al [th]i gilt.
Thi praier I schal fulfille—
140 Loke on me, yif that thou wilt.

Therwhiles that thou art hayl and quert,
Biheld me wele, everich a bon.
Bithenche in thine owhen hert
That warisoun no hastow non.
145 Thine axing sore schal the smert
Yif thou be blinde as ani ston.
Thou most live in gret povert
[W]hen thou hast thine eiyen forgon:
When thou forgos thi warldes wele,
150 And love of frendes, fremed and sibbe,
Angwis thou most suffri fele
In alle time that thou schalt libbe."

The clerk answerd and lough,

138 [th]i, *MS has* mi.   150 fremed, *MS
has* feremed, *with the first
e apparently struck out.*

---

127 that I the bad] what I asked you   128 Efsones]
Again   130 that] when   137 the clerk . . .
untille] to the clerk   141 quert] whole
142 everich a bon] every single bone
143 Bithenche] Consider   144 warisoun]
reward   149 wele] welfare   150 fremed and
sibbe] unrelated persons and kinsmen   151 fele]
cruel   153 lough] laughed

"Min hert is ful of gret solas.
155 Icham blither than brid on bough
That ich have seyn thine holy face.
Of al joie ichave anough.
Sende me now, Levedi, of thi grace.
To suffren wo mi bodi is tough
160 Bi so ich mot haven a place:
A place graunt me, Marie,
That mi soule mot wone
With joie and with melodye
In Heven bifor thi swet sone."

165 Sche seyd, "Mi clerk, no wepe thou nought,
No make no mornand chere;
Thi bon thou hast me bisought
Ich graunt the in al maner.
Into that joie thou schalt be brought
170 When thou hast laten thi liif here,
That mi swete sone hath wrought
To hem that ben him leve and dere:
Dere thou art to me, ywis.
Oyain to Heven now ich mot wende
175 And thou schalt com into that blis
When thou hast laten thi lives ende."

Up into Heven anon sche steyye
Ther sche is quen and levedi corn.
The clerk his eiyen fast he wreiye:
180 He wende his sight were forlorn.
When it was day, ful wele he seiye
This warldes pride al him biforn.
"Merci, Levedi!" he crid on heiye.
"Wele be the time that thou were born!
185 That thou were born of o wiman
Blisced be ever the day!

180 forlorn, *second* r *added above the line.*
181 day, *inserted above the line.*

---

155 brid] bird   160 Bi so]
Provided that   166 mornand chere]
sad expression   167 bon] request   170 laten]
left   177 steyye] ascended   178 Ther] Where
corn] chosen   179 wreiye] covered   185 o] a

Ther liveth nowight that telle can
The joie that of the springeth ay.

Levedi, flour and frout of Jesse,
190 Thou art maiden, gode and hende;
Godes moder, mild and fre,
Michel thou helpest al mankende.
On thi servaunt have pite
And save ous, Lord, fram the Fende,
195 And graunt ous, yif thi wille be,
When we schul of this warld wende:
When we schul wend out of this live,
Here our prayer and our steven:
Bring ous, for thine joies five,
200 Into the swete blis of Heven."

187 nowight] no one   190 hende] gentle
191 fre] generous   194ff. *The references to Our
Lord and Our Lady are confused.*   198 steven]
voice

How Chartres Was Saved

Fol. 123ᵇ

Lordus, yif ye wol, lusten to me.
Of Croteye, the noble cite,
Furst hou hit biseget was
And sethen dilyveret thorw Godus gras
5 And thorw the help of Ure Ladi:
So witnesseth miracle of Mari.
Out of Peihtes-Lond ther came
A kniht that Rollo was his name.
He gederet with him out of the north cost
10 Of diverse nacions a wel gret host,
Out of Denemarch and North-Wey
Of feolore folk then I con sey.
Mony cuntres he can destruye;
Wel muchel pepule he gan anuye.
15 In mony a coost, bi est and west,
He won him londes bi conquest.
Furst he bigon in the north cuntre,
And aftur he schipet over the see.
Sire Rollo, with al his host,
20 Arivede in Fraunce up in a cost.
That cuntre gon he furst destruiye;
Therfore he called hit Northmondye,

2 Croteye] Chartres   4 sethen] afterward
7 Peihtes-Lond] Scotland   11 North-Wey]
Norway   12 feolore] more   13 can] did
14 anuye] molest   18 schipet] took ship

30

For thei dude men to dethe ilome
That out of the north cost come:
25 Therfore he called hit Northmondye,
As writen I fynde in his storye.
Of Bruit the Cronicle witnesset wel
This conquest of Rollo everidel.
Hit was the furste duik in that lond,
30 For he furst won hit with his hond.
Whon Rollo that kniht was thider icomen,
And mony a toun thei hedde inomen,
Mony a mon thei dude to dethe:
Ful fewe thei saveden and yit unnethe.
35 And as he travayled on his jorney,
He com to a citee was called Crotey.
Thus sone Sire Rollo, with his route,
Bisette that citee with sege aboute.
Withinne the citee men hedde gret drede,
40 Heore enemys weren so douhti of dede:
Of socour thei seyen non othur won
But yelden the cite or elles ben slon.
An holi bisschop ther was therinne
That was called Sire Waltelinne.
45 He was bisschop of that citee;
A swuythe noble mon was he.
He tauhte heom yerne knele and crie
To Crist and to his modur Marie.
Thorw help of hire that bar Ur Lord
50 He hopede thei schulden han sone cumfort.
Sethen himself goth to the sextriye
That was the munstres treserye.
Ur Ladi curtel therinne he found;
With gret reverence he kneled to ground.
55 Ther to Marie he beed his bone,
To sende that cite socour sone.
With peple and gret processioun

23 Because they frequently put people to death
28 everidel] completely   32 inomen] taken
34 unnethe] with difficulty   37 route] retinue
40 Heore] Their   41 seyen] saw   won] hope
46 swuythe] very   47 yerne] earnestly   crie]
pray   51 sextriye] sacristy   53 curtel] gown
55 beed his bone] made his prayer

He bar that relyk thorw al the toun
Ful deyntely diht uppon a spere
60 As lordus baner displayet in werre.
The Bisschop heet cast up the yate
And bad his folk folewe hym algate,
Himself biforen and thei behynde:
He hoped in Marie help to fynde.
65 Anon, as thei were thus out went,
Heore enemys letten hem not but schent,
For so astoneyd and ferede men
Nere never worse then thei were then:
Whon on that relyk thei caste heore siht,
70 Thei woxe start blynde anon riht.
Thei mihten no more defenden heom then
Then so mony blynde or drounkne men:
The citeseins token hem at heore wille,
Summe to raunsum, and summe to spille.
75 Sithen thei turnen ayeyn to the citee
With murthe and gret solempnite,
And herieden heihly that mylde may
That socourde and saved hem so that day.
And do we on the same wyse,
80 Bothe glade and blithe with bisy servise,
The same ladi forte qweme
That so in mischeef to us taketh yeme
To hire sone Crist ure erende to bede,
And socoureth us so at everi nede.
85 Nou, Ladi, preye thi sone on hih
To alle Cristene he graunte merci.

59 diht] arranged   61 heet cast up the yate]
ordered that the gate be cast up   66 Their
enemies did not stop them but fell into disorder
67 ferede] frightened   70 start blynde] stark
blind   74 spille] put to death   77 herieden]
praised   may] maiden   81 forte qweme] in
order to please   82 yeme] care   83 erende]
petition

The Child Slain by Jews

Fol. 124

Wose loveth wel Ure Ladi,
Heo wol quiten his wille wel whi,
Othur in his lyf or at his ende,
The ladi is so freo and hende.
5 Hit fel sum tyme in Parys,
As witnesseth in holy writ storys,
In the cite bifel this cas:
A pore child was of porchas
That with the beggeri that he con wynne
10 He fond sumdel what of his kinne,
His fader, his moder, and eke himself;
He begged in cite bi everi half.
The child non othur craftus couthe,
But winne his lyflode with his mouthe.
15 The childes vois was swete and cler;
Men lusted his song with riht good cher.
With his song that was ful swete,
He gat mete from strete to strete.
Men herked his song ful likyngly:
20 Hit was an antimne of Ure Lady.
He song that antimne everiwher
Icalled "Alma Redemptoris Mater";
That is forthrihtly to mene,
"Godus Moder, mylde and clene,
25 Hevene yate and sterre of se,
Save thi peple from synne and we."
That song was holden deynteous;
The child song hit from hous to hous.
For he song hit so lykynglye,

1 Wose] Whoever   2 She will reward his will
well for that(?); *meaning of* whi *uncertain*   4 freo
and hende] generous and gracious   8 porchas]
property   9 beggeri] proceeds of begging
10 He supported some of his relatives   12 bi
everi half] everywhere   14 winne his lyflode]
earn his living   16 lusted] listened to
25 Hevene yate] Heaven's gate   26 we] woe
27 deynteous] excellent   29 lykynglye] attrac-
tively

30 The Jewes hedde alle to hym envye,
Til hit fel on a Setersday
The childes wey thorw the Jewerie lay.
The Jewes hedden that song in hayn;
Therfore thei schope the child be slayn.
35 So lykingly the child song ther
So lustily song he never er.
On of the Jewes malicious
Tilled the child into his hous.
His malice there he gan to kuythe:
40 He cutte the childes throte alswithe.
The child ne spared nout for that wrong,
But never-the-latere song forth his song.
Whon he hedde endet, he eft bigon:
His syngyng couthe stoppe no mon.
45 Therof the Jeuh was sore anuyet,
Leste his malice mihte ben aspyet.
The Jeuh bithouhte him of a gynne:
Into a gonge-put, fer withinne,
The child adoun therinne he throng;
50 The child song evere the same song.
So lustily the child con crie
That song he never er so hyhe:
Men mihte him here fer and neer,
The childes vois was so heih and cleer.
55 The childes moder was wont to abyde
Every day til the nontyde;
Then was he wont to bringe heom mete,
Such as he mihte with his song gete.
Bote that day was the tyme apast;
60 Therfore his moder was sore agast.
With syk and serwe in everi strete
Heo souhte wher heo mihte with him mete,
Bote whon heo com into the Jewery,
Heo herde his vois, so cler of cry.

30 envye] malice   33 hayn] hatred
34 schope] brought about   38 Tilled] Enticed
39 kuythe] make known   40 alswithe]
immediately   42 never-the-latere] nevertheless
45 anuyet] troubled   47 gynne] scheme
48 gonge-put] privy pit   49 throng] thrust
51 con] did   57 heom] them   61 syk] sigh

65 Aftur that vois his modur dreuh;
Wher he was inne, therbi heo kneuh.
Then of hire child heo asked a siht;
The Jew withnayted him anon riht,
And seide ther nas non such child thrinne.

70 The childes moder yit nolde not blinne,
But ever the moder criede in on.
The Jeuh seide evere ther nas such non.
Then seide the wommon, "Thou seist wrong!
He is herinne. I knowe his song."

75 The Jeuh bigon to stare and swere,
And seide ther com non such child there;
But never-the-latere, men mihte here:
The child song evere so loude and clere,
And ever the lengor, herre and herre,

80 Men mihte him here bothe fer and nerre.
The modur coude non othur won;
To meir and baylyfs heo is gon.
Heo pleyneth the Jeuh hath don hire wrong
To stelen hire sone so for his song.

85 Heo preyeth to don hire lawe and riht,
Hire sone don come bifore heore siht.
Heo preyeth the meir *par charité*
Of him to have freo lyvere.
Thenne heo telleth the meir among

90 Hou heo lyveth bi hire sone song.
The meir then hath of hire pite,
And sumneth the folk of that cite;
He telleth hem of that wommons sawe,
And seith he mot don hire the lawe,

95 And hoteth hem with hym to wende
To bringe this wommons cause to ende.
Whon thei cum thider, for al heore noyse,
Anon thei herde the childes voyse.
Riht as an angls vois hit were:

68 withnayted] denied   69 thrinne] therein
70 blinne] cease   71 in on] continually
79 herre] higher   81 won] hope   85 lawe]
justice   86 Hire sone don come] Make her son
come   88 lyvere] legal delivery   89 among]
meanwhile   93 sawe] story   95 hoteth hem]
commands them

100 Thei herde him never synge so clere.
Ther the meir maketh entre,
And of the child he asketh lyvere.
The Jeuh may nouht the meir refuse,
Ne of the child hym wel excuse,
105 But nede he moste knouleche his wrong,
Ateynt bi the childes song.
The meir let serchen hym so longe
Til he was founden in the gonge,
Ful depe idrouned in fulthe of fen.
110 The meir het drawe the child up then,
With fen and fulthe riht foule biwhorven,
And eke the childes throte icorven.
Anon riht, er thei passede forthere,
The Jeuh was jugget for that morthere,
115 And er the peple passede in sonder,
The bisschop was comen to seo that wonder.
In presence of bisschop and alle ifere,
The child song evere iliche clere.
The bisschop serchede with his hond.
120 Withinne the childes throte he fond
A lilie flour, so briht and cler,
So feir a lylie nas nevere seyen er,
With guldene lettres everiwher:
"Alma Redemptoris Mater."
125 Anon, that lilie out was taken;
The childes song bigon to slaken.
That swete song was herd no more,
But as a ded cors the child lay thore.
The bisschop, with gret solempnete,
130 Bad bere the cors thorw al the cite,
And hymself, with processioun,
Com with the cors thorw al the toun,
With prestes and clerkes that couthen syngen,
And alle the belles he het hem ryngen.
135 With torches brennynge and clothus riche,

106 Ateynt] Proved guilty
109 fen] dung   110 het drawe the child up]
commanded that the child be drawn up
111 biwhorven] bespattered   117 ifere] together
118 iliche] equally   128 cors] corpse   thore]
there

36

With worschipe thei ladden that holi liche.
Into the munstre whon thei kem
Bigonne the Masse of Requiem,
As for the dede men is wont;
140 But thus sone thei weren istunt:
The cors aros in heore presens,
Bigon then "Salve, Sancta Parens."
Men mihte wel witen the sothe therbi:
The child hedde iservet ur swete Ladi,
145 That worschipede him so on erthe her
And brouhte his soule to blisse al cler.
Therfore I rede that everi mon
Serve that ladi wel as he con,
And love hire in his beste wyse:
150 Heo wol wel quite him his servise.
Now, Marie, for thi muchele miht,
Help us to Hevene that is so briht!

138 Requiem, *MS blurred by an illustration on reverse.*   145 erthe, *preceded by a mark partially obliterated, which may have been* S.

---

136 liche] body   140 istunt] stunned
145 worschipede] honored   147 rede] advise

The Jewish Boy

Foll. 124^b-125

Lord, makere of alle thing,
Almihti God in majeste,
That ever was withoute biginning
And art and evermore schal be,
5   Graunte us bothe miht and space
So to serve the to pay,
That we mowe thorw thi grace
Wone with the for evere and ay.
Of the miracles of Ure Ladi
10   We ouhten wel to haven in muynde
That writen beth in soth stori
Hou helplich heo is evere to monkynde.
Sumtyme fel in on cite—
Herkneth wel, and ye may here—
15   As Jewes weren iwont to be
Among the Cristen and wone ifere,
The Cristene woneden in on halve
Of that cite, as I the hete,
And alle the Jewes bi hemselve
20   Were stihlet to wone in a strete.
The Cristene children in a crofte
Imad hem hedden a wel feir plas.
Therinne a Jewes child ful ofte
With hem to pleyen iwont he was.
25   The childes fader nom non hede,
Ne to his child he sette non eiye.
Therfore the child bothe com and eode
As ofte as evere hem luste to pleye.
So ofte to pleyen hem fel ifere

6 pay] please   8 Wone] Dwell   10 muynde]
mind   12 heo] she   13 Once it happened in
a city   15 iwont] accustomed   16 ifere]
together   18 as I the hete] as I assure you
20 stihlet] assigned   a] one   21 crofte] field
22 hem] them   25 nom non hede] took no
notice   27 eode] went   28 luste] pleased
29 So often they happened to play together

30 The Jewes sone on heore pleyes coude,
     That riht as on of hem he were.
     With love, therfore, thei him alouwede.
     At an Astertyme bitidde,
     Whon Cristen made solempnite—
35 A menskful munstre was mad amidde,
     As semed best, in that citee.
     Therto the Cristene peple can drawe
     To here bothe mateyns and eke masse,
     As falleth bi the Cristene lawe
40 Bothe to more and eke to lasse,
     Everi mon in his array,
     Bothe housbonde and wyf also,
     As falleth wel for Asterday
     And al as Cristene men schul do.
45 The children foleweden heore fadres in fere,
     As thei weore evere iwont to do;
     The Jewes child with wel good chere
     With hem wel fayn was for to go.
     Withinne the chirche whon he was riht,
50 Him thouhte he nas never er so glad
     As he was of that semeli siht.
     Such on bifore never seye he had:
     Bothe laumpes and tapers breninnde briht
     And auters curiousliche depeynt,
55 Images ful deinteousliche idiht,
     And guld of moni a good corseynt.
     A comeli qween in o chayer
     Ful semeli sat, al greithed in golde;
     A blisful babe on arm heo beer
60 Ful kyngly corouned, as he scholde.
     Of that ladi the child tok hede,
     And of that blisful babe also,

30 The Jew's son knew their games   33 Aster-
tyme] Eastertime   35 menskful] stately
37 can] did   41 array] apparel   45 in fere]
together   48 fayn] eager   52 Such on] Such
a one seye] seen   54 curiousliche depeynt]
skilfully decorated   55 deinteousliche idiht]
excellently arrayed   56 And gilt of many a
goodly shrine of a saint   57 o] a   58 greithed]
dressed   59 blisful] blessed beer] bore

Hou folk biforen heore bedes bede
As Cristen men beth wont to do.
65 The Jewes child evere tok such yeme
To alle sihtes that he ther seih,
Him thouhte hem alle so swete to seme
For joye him thouhte iravessched neih.
Whon heih masse of that day was do,
70 The prest bad alle men knelen adoun.
With "Confiteor," as falleth therto,
He yiveth hem absolucioun.
He biddeth hem more and lasse also
To vengen heor saviour busken hem boun.
75 The Jewes child tok tente therto.
Among the Cristene he dude him doun.
Among the pres thauh he were poselet,
He spared nothing for no drede
Among the Cristene til he were hoselet.
80 Of such a child me tok non hede.
To ende whon alle thing was brouht
And everi Cristene drouh him hom,
The Jeuh thorw toune his child hath souht,
And saih wher he from chirche com.
85 He asked his sone wher he hedde ben,
Whil he hedde souht him al that day.
Al, riht as he hedde idon and seon,
The child him rikenet al the aray.
His fader therfore wox wood-wroth,
90 And seide anon, "Thou getest thi mede!"
And to his hovene al hot he goth,
That glemede as glowyng as a glede.
Into the hovene the child he caste.
To askes he thouhte the child to brenne,

63 heore bedes bede] said their prayers
65 yeme] heed   74 vengen] receive busken
hem boun] make themselves ready   75 tente]
attention   76 dude him doun] knelt
77 poselet] bewildered   79 til he were hoselet]
until he should have received Communion
80 me] *indefinite pronoun*; me tok non hede:
people paid no attention   88 rikenet] told
89 wood-wroth] angry to madness   92 glede]
live coal   94 askes] ashes

95 And with the mouth-ston he steketh him faste,
   And thouhte that never couth scholde him kenne.
   Therof whon his moder herde,
   In a stude ther as heo stood,
   As frayed in frenesye heo ferde;
100 For wo heo wente as waxen wood.
   Ever hotyng out, heo tar hire her
   In everi stret of that citee,
   Nou in, nou out, so everiwher:
   Men wondret on hire and hedde pite.
105 Bothe meir and bailifs of the toun,
   Whon thei herden of that cri,
   Thei aresten hire bi resoun
   A[nd] maden chalange enchesun whi
   Heo criede so in that cite
110 And putte the peple in such affray
   To serwen in such solempnite
   And nomeliche on heore Asterday.
   As sone as heo mihte sece of wepe,
   This was the seyinge of hire sawe:
115 "Sires, ye han this citee to kepe,
   As lordus han to lede the lawe.
   Allas, allas, I am ischent,
   And help of ow me mot bihoven.
   I prey ow of just juggement:
120 Mi cause I schal bifore you proven.
   Mi hosebonde hath my child ibrent,
   Istopped him in a glouwyng hoven.
   Goth seoth, Sires, bi on assent,
   And I schal yive ow gold to gloven."
125 Bothe meir and baylifs, with folk ifere,
   To the Jewes hovene ben gon.

95 he steketh him faste] he fastens
him tightly   96 couth scholde
him kenne] acquaintance should find him out
98 stude] place   99 She acted as if frightened
into a frenzy   101 hotyng out] calling out   heo
tar hire her] she tore her hair   107 bi resoun]
with good reason   108 enchesun whi] the reason
why   111 To sorrow in such a public manner
114 sawe] story   118 And help from you must
be due me   124 gold to gloven] gold as a
reward(?)

As sone as thei thider come were,
The meir comaundet, "Doth doun the ston!"
Ther everi mon wel mihte iseo
130 The hovene roof, that was so round,
Hou hit was blasyng al of bleo
As glouwyng glos, from roof to grount.
The child sat there, bothe hol and sound,
Ne nouht iharmet, hond ny her,
135 Amidde the gledes of the ground
As he seete in cool erber.
The childes moder, whon heo that seih,
Hire thouhte heo nas never er so glad.
Into the hovene heo sturte him neih;
140 Thus sone with hire him out heo had.
And al the peple there present
Wondred on that selly siht,
And heried God with good entent,
For miracle is more then monnes miht.
145 Hou he hath non harmes hent
Among the brondes that brenneth so briht,
Thei asken of him bi on assent.
The child onswered anon riht,
"Of alle the murthes that I have had
150 In al my lyf hiderto,
Ne was I nevere of gleo so glad
As aftur I was in the hovene ido.
Bothe brondes and gledes, trustily,
That weren binethen undur my fote,
155 As feire floures, feithfully,
As special spices me thouhte hem swote.
The blisful qwen, that maiden milde,
That sitteth in chirche in hih chayer
With that comely kyng, hire childe
160 (That blisful babe on barm heo ber),

147 Thei, *MS blurred.*   149 had, *MS blurred.*

---

131 bleo] livid appearance
132 glos] glass   134 hond ny her] hand nor
hair   136 erber] grassy place   139 sturte]
jumped   142 selly] blessed   143 heried]
praised   145 hent] taken   152 ido] put
156 swote] sweet   160 barm] bosom

From alle the schydes thei cunne me schilde:
From gledes and brondes that brende so cler,
From alle the flaumes that flowen so wilde,
That never non mihte neihhe me ner."

165 Bothe men and wymmen, al that ther were,
Thei herieden God hertily,
Bothe luytel and muche, lasse and more,
Of this miracle, witerly.
The Jewesse, thorw hire sones sawe,

170 Was convertet to Crist anon.
The child tok hym to Cristes lawe,
And alle the Jewes, everichon.
The meir sat on the Jeuh himselve,
Forte beo juge of his trespas.

175 To siggen the sothe, isworen were twelve
To yiven heore verdyt in that caas.
Thei counseiled ivere uppon that caas
And comen ayeyn bi on assent.
The wordes of that verdyt was,

180 "In that same hovene he schulde be brent."
Thus is endet this stori
Of the miracle
Iwriten above.
God graunt us joy

185 In Hevene an hih,
Jhesu, for thi moder love.

161 schydes] firewood   164 That none might
ever come near me   167 luytel] little
168 witerly] without doubt   171 tok hym]
betook himself   173 sat on] sat in judgment upon
174 Forte] In order to   175 To siggen] To tell
177 ivere] together

43

The Merchant's Surety

At Constantynnoble, in that cite,
Dwelled a marchaunt of herte fre,
Sumtyme was riche, ful of lewte,
And after fel in poverte,
5 And, as the bokes telles us,
He was iclept Theodorus.
He lovede God and Ure Ladi,
And served that mayden speciali.
And in that cite, sothliche,
10 A Jeuh ther dwelled, was wonder riche.
In his lay he hedde good name;
He was iclepet Abrahame.
Theodorus he lovede wele;
Gret lykyng hedde with him to dele.
15 Theodorus hedde thouht and care,
For he nedde not with to chaffare.
He caste him therfore to borwe;
To the Jeuh he wente amorwe.
Ther he told him his mischeef
20 And preiede hym of sum releef,
Of his gold him for to lene,
And thus to hym he gon hym mene.
The Jeuh onswerde with gret honour,
"Loke hou thou maiht make me seur
25 Me to paye at certeyn day,
And the to helpe I schal assay."
Theodorus seide, "Icham behynde,
For me ther wol no mon hym bynde.
He that sumtyme was my fere
30 Me passeth bi withouten chere.
But yif thou dorstest be so hardi
To take Ur Ladi, Seinte Mari,

2 fre] generous   3 lewte] fidelity   11 lay]
religion   16 For he had nothing with which to
trade   17 He caste him] He resolved   19 mis-
cheef] trouble   22 hym mene] complain
23 honour] respect   29 fere] friend   30 chere]
facial expression

44

For my borw, be mi fay,
I schulde the pay wel at thi day."

35 The Jeuh seide, "My goode feere,
I graunte the, Sire, thi preyere,
For I have herd oftesithe
That ladi is corteis and blithe.
Men seith heo wol hem never fayle
40 That in hire servise wol travayle.
Therfore go we into your chirche,
And ther this forward we wol worche.
Ther is an ymage of hire iliche
Arayed wel with juweles riche.
45 Tac thou hire me ther bi the hond;
Of the kep I non othur bond."
Whon he hed seid, thei gonne to gon;
To that churche thei comen anon.
Theodorus in good manere
50 Kneled adoun, bad his preyere,
And aftur that with good visage
Went hym up to that ymage
And tok hit bi that on hond,
And bad the Jeuh scholde to him fond,
55 And seide, "Sire, so God me save,
For my borwh this ladi have,
That I shal paye the at my day
Treweliche and wel al thi monay
That thou schalt me nou take,
60 Al my disese with to slake."
The Jeuh him tok a summe of gold,
Good moneye and wel itold,
And sette hym ther a certeyn day
Him to paye hit withoute delay.
65 The Cristen mon then was ful fayn;
They wenten hom ful fayn ayayn,

33 borw] surety   be mi fay]
by my faith   39 heo] she   hem] them   42 this
forward we wol worche] we will execute this
agreement   43 iliche] alike   45 There take her
by the hand for me [as a pledge]   50 bad his
preyere] said his prayer   53 bi that on hond] by
the one hand   54 fond] draw near(?)
59 take] give   65 fayn] happy

45

And he arrayed him ful fast
A schip with seil and eke a mast.
To Alysaundre he gon sayle;
70 Ther he aryved withouten fayle.
Thenne he bouhte faste and solde,
And everi day the pons tolde.
He won faste day by day;
The yeer passed sone away.
75 He thouhte so muche on his wynnyng,
Foryat the day of his payyng
Til the even was icomen
Amorwe schulde paye that he hedde nomen.
Hit fel into his muynde thon
80 He schulde bi holde a fals mon.
To that cuntre so fer atwynne
In so schort while miht he not wynne
Forte holde his day of paye,
Bote to Ur Ladi he gon to praye
85 Hym to counseyle and to rede
What mihte thenne be his beste spede,
And cast hit in herte outurly
To truste in God and Ure Ladi.
He tok hym thenne a luytel kyst.
90 Therinne he putte, that no wiht wist,
The summe of gold, verreyment,
That the Jeuh hedde hym ilent,
And a lettre, that seide thus:
"This to Abraham Jeuh sent Theodorus."
95 Aftur that, with his hond,
Aboute with iren he hit bond.
Into the see then he hit cast,
Preied Ur Ladi ben schip and mast
Hit to save in Godes nam
100 To the Jeuh Abraham.

72 pons] pennies
78 that he hedde nomen] that which
he had taken   79 muynde] mind   80 holde]
considered   81 so fer atwynne] so far apart
83 Forte] In order to   85 rede] advise
86 spede] help   87 outurly] utterly   89 luytel
kyst] little chest   90 that no wiht wist] so that
no one knew   99 save] deliver safely

The Jeuh aros uppon the morn,
As I ow telle withoute scorn,
And stilliche forth gon he stalke
To the see-syde, ther forte walke,
105 That ebbet and flowed faste bi his house
Ther he dwellede and his spouse.
Soone he was war wel inouh
Of a cofre, touward hym drouh,
Floterynge in that salte see:
110 Gret wonder he hedde what hit miht be.
Ful sone to hym he hit up nom;
Undur his arm he bar hit hom.
He fond therinne, verrement,
The gold that he hedde furst and lent.
115 Beo the lettre he wuste also
From what mon that hit com fro.
He caste hit thenne into an ark
That was bothe styf and stark.
To telle therof no wiht him luste
120 But wente him forth as no wiht wuste.
Longe afturward, in Godes nome,
Theodorus was comen home.
With him ther mette mony on
That him welcomede swithe son.
125 With Abraham the Jeuh he mette;
Ful corteysliche he hym grette,
And thonked hym of his fordede,
And preied God schulde quite his mede.
The Jeuh seide, "So mot I the,
130 I trouwe that thou scorne me.
Whi hast thou broken thi terme-day
Of the payyement of mi monay?"
Theodorus seide, "Thou wost wel
I have the payed everidel.

102 ow] you withoute scorn]
without jest 106 Ther]
Where 115 Beo] By 117 ark] box
118 stark] strong 121 nome] name
124 swithe] very 127 fordede] favor
128 quite his mede] reward him

47

135 I take my borwh to my witnesse,
    I owe the nouther more no lesse.
    Go we to churche bothe ifere,
    And ther the sothe thou schalt here."
    "I graunte wel," quath the Jewe.
140 "But thou me paye thou schalt hit rewe."
    The Jew made hit wonder touh,
    And wende hit hedde beo good inouh.
    Whon thei were bifore that ymage
    That for the gold was mad his gage,
145 Theodorus seide with mylde stevene,
    "Ladi, as thou art Qween of Hevene,
    Help me nou from worldly schome.
    I preye the in thi sones nome.
    Thou wost wel, Ladi, ther thou sist,
150 I putte the gold into a kist,
    And to this Jeuh that hit schulde wende,
    I preyed the hit to him sende.
    As I truste on thi sone and the,
    Ladi, the sothe scheuh for me."
155 The ymage spac, as God hit wolde,
    And seide, "Jeuh, thou hast thi golde,
    And in the botme of thyn ark
    Ther thou hast leid everi mark."
    The Jewh wox aschomed tho
160 And graunted wel that hit was so.
    Alle that leeved on his lay
    Aschomed weren that ilke day.
    Ther he hedde saumple bi good dome
    Cristene mon forte bicome.
165 This ladi is ful gracius
    That thenketh evere thus on us.
    Therfore to hire loke thou be trewe,
    And chaunge we hire not for non newe.
    Heo wole us helpe in ure mischeef

136 nouther more no lesse]
neither more nor less   141 touh]
tough; made hit wonder touh: made things very
hard   144 gage] pledge   149 ther thou sist]
where you sit   154 scheuh] show   161 that
leeved on his lay] that believed in his law
163 There he had example by good judgment

170 In this world to us releef,
  And afturward, withouten mis,
  Geten us Hevene-riche blis
  Thorw the grace of hire sone,
  With him there forte wone,
175 And that hit mote so be
  Seith alle "Amen," *par charité.*

THOMAS HOCCLEVE

HM 744 (early fifteenth century),
Huntington Library

The Monk and Our Lady's Sleeves

Text from HM 744 (early fifteenth century; foll. 36-
39ᵇ), Huntington Library (*A*); variant readings
from MS. 152 (1460-1500; foll. 229-231), Christ
Church College, Oxford (*B*), and from MS. R.3.21
(ca. 1442-1483; foll. 274ᵇ-275ᵇ), Trinity College,
Cambridge (*C*). Starred readings are common to *B*
and *C* with minor variations in form.

Whoso desirith to gete and conquere
The blisse of Hevene, needful is a guyde
Him to condue and for to brynge him there;
And so good knowe I noon for mannes syde
5   As the roote of humblesse and fo to pryde,
That lady of whos tetes virginal
Sook our redemptour, the makere of al.

Betwixt God and man is shee mediatrice
For oure offenses mercy to purchace.
10   Shee is our seur sheeld ageyn the malice
Of the feend, that our soules wolde embrace
And carie hem unto that horrible place
Whereas eternel peyne is and torment
More than may be spoke of, thoght, or ment.

3 condue] lead   7 Sook] Sucked   10 seur] sure

2 needful] *B*, *C* holsom   3 and . . . there] *B* and hym
to brynge there; *C* and to bryng there   4 And] *not in C*
5 to] *C* unto   8 is shee] *C* she ys   10 Shee . . .
sheeld] *B*, *C* She owre sheld ys*   13 Whereas . . . is]
B Whereas peyne ay duryng ys; *C* Where ys a peyne ay
duryng   14 spoke . . . ment] *B*, *C* spoken of or ment*

15 Now syn that lady noble and glorious
    To al mankynde hath so greet cheertee
    That in this slipir lyf and perillous
    Staf of confort and help to man is shee,
    Convenient is that to that lady free
20 We do service, honour, and plesance,
    And to that ende, heere is a remembrance.

    Ther was whilom, as that seith the scripture,
    In France a ryche man and a worthy,
    That God and Holy Chirche to honure
25 And plese enforced he him bisily,
    And unto Crystes modir specially,
    That noble lady, that blissid virgyne,
    For to worsshipe he dide his might and pyne.

    It shoop so that this man had a yong sone,
30 Unto which he yaf informacion
    Every day to have in custume and wone
    For to seye, at his excitacion,
    The Angelike Salutacion
    Fifty sythes in worship and honour
35 Of Goddes modir, of vertu the flour.

    By his fadres wil a monk, aftirward,
    In th'Abbeye of Seint Gyle maad was he,
    Whereas he in penance sharp and hard
    Observed wel his ordres duetee,

21 *MS has* Explicit prologus et incipit fabula *after the line.*

16 cheertee] affection   17 slipir]
uncertain   19 Convenient] Fitting   free]
generous   25 enforced] exerted   28 worsshipe]
honor   pyne] pain   29 It shoop so] It so
happened   31 wone] habit   34 sythes] times

15 syn] *C* sythen   19 is] *C* hit ys   21 is] *not in C*
22 Ther . . . scripture] *C* Whylom there was as seyth
scrypture   23 a worthy] *C* worthy   24 to] *C* dyd
25 And . . . bisily] *B* And plese enforced hym ful bysyly;
C And to plese enforsyd hym besyly   26 And . . .
specially] *C* Crystys modyr most specially   27 noble]
C glorious blissid] *C* blyssful   29 that] *not in C*
30 which] *C* the whyche   31 to have] *not in C*
35 Goddes] *B, C* Cristys*   the flour] *B* myrroure, *C* the
myrrour

40 Lyvynge in vertuous religioustee,
And on a tyme, him to pleye and solace,
His fadir made him come hoom to his place.

Now was ther at Our Ladyes reverence
A chapel in it maad and edified,
45 Into which the monk, whan convenience
Of tyme he had awayted and espied,
His fadres lore to fulfille him hied,
And fifty sythes, with devout corage,
Seide "Ave Marie," as was his usage.

50 And whan that he had endid his preyeere,
Our Lady, clothid in a garnement
Sleevelees, byfore him he sy appeere,
Whereof the monk took good avisament,
Merveillynge him what that this mighte han ment,
55 And seide, "O goode Lady, by your leeve,
What garnament is this and hath no sleeve?"

And she answerde and seide, "This clothynge
Thow hast me yoven, for thow every day,
Fifty sythe 'Ave Maria' seyynge,
60 Honured hast me. Hens foorth, I the pray,
Use to treble that by any way,
And to every tenthe 'Ave' joyne also
A 'Pater noster,' do thow evene so.

The firste fifti wole I that seid be
65 In the memorie of the joie and honour
That I had whan the angel grette me,
Which was right a wondirful confortour
To me whan he seide the redemptour

43 at] for   44 edified] built   51 garnement]
garment   52 sy] saw   53 avisament] thought
58 yoven] given

42 come] C to come   45 Into which] B In the whyche;
C Into the whyche   46 he had] not in C   50 And . . .
preyeere] B And when he had y-endyd hys prayere; C
And when the monke had endyd hys prayere
54 Merveillynge . . . ment] C Mervelyng moche what thys
ment   55 O] not in B, C   57 And] not in B
62 And] not in B, C   'Ave'] not in B   63 thow] B,
C ryght   67 wondirful] C worde full

Of al mankynde I receyve sholde.
70 Greet was my joie whan he so me tolde.

Thow shalt eek seyn the seconde fifty
In honur and in mynde of the gladnesse
That I had whan I baar of my body
God and man withouten wo or duresse.
75 The thridde fifty in thyn herte impresse
And seye it eek with good devocioun
In the memorie of myn assumpcioun,

Whan that I was coroned Queene of Hevene
In which my sone regneth and shal ay."
80 Al this was doon that I speke of and meene,
As the book seith, upon an halyday.
And than seide Our Lady, the glorious may,
"The nexte halyday wole I resorte
To this place, thee to glade and conforte."

85 And therwithal, fro thens departed shee,
The monk in his devocion dwellynge;
And every day, "Ave Maria" he
Seide, aftir hir doctryne and enformynge.
And the nexte haliday aftir suynge,
90 Our Lady, fresshly arraied and wel,
To the monk cam, beynge in that chapel,

And unto him seide, "Beholde now
How good clothyng and how fressh apparaille
That this wyke to me yoven hast thow.
95 Sleeves to my clothynge now nat faille:
Thee thanke I, and ful wel for thy travaille

82 may] maiden   89 suynge] following

---

69 receyve] B, C conceyve*
76 And . . . devocioun] C And sey
them with good devocion   78 that] not in B
80 meene] B, C neven*   81 seith] C telleth
82 Omitted in C   the] B that   83 wole I] C I wyll
87 And . . . he] B And every day suyng here psalter he;
C And every day aftyr hyr sawter he seyde   88 Seide]
not in C   89 suynge] B, C folwyng*   91 To the monk
cam] C Came to the monke   that] B, C the   92 And . . .
seide] B, C And to hym seyde shee*   93 fressh] B, C
good

53

Shalt thow be qwit heere in this lyf present
And in that othir whan thow hens art went.

Walke now, and go hoom unto th'abbeye.
100 Whan thow comst, abbot shalt thow chosen be;
And the covent teche thow for to seye
My psalter, as byforn taght have I thee.
The peple also thow shalt in generaltee
The same lessoun to myn honur teche,
105 And in hire hurtes wole I been hir leche.

Sevene yeer lyve shalt thow for to do
This charge, and whan tho yeeres been agoon
Thow passe shalt hens and me come unto.
And of this doute have thow right noon:
110 By my psalter shal ther be many oon
Saved and had up to eternel blisse
That, if that nere, sholden thereof misse."

Whan shee had seid what lykid hire to seye,
Shee up to Hevene ascendid up and sty,
115 And soone aftir, abbot of that abbeye
He maad was, as that tolde him Our Lady.
The covent and the peple devoutly
This monk enformed, and taghte hir psalteer
For to be seid, aftir that sevene yeer.

120 Tho yeeres past, his soule was betaght
To God; he Hevene had unto his meede.

97 qwit] rewarded
101 covent] monastery   105 leche] physician
114 sty] rose   120 betaght] entrusted

99 Walke ... th'abbeye] C Walke now home to
thyne abbey   unto] B to   100 shalt thow chosen be]
B, C chosyn shalt thow be   101 And the covent] B And
to the covent   for] not in C   103 The] C Thy
104 to] B unto   teche] B, C preche   105 in] B, C of
hire] not in C   108 Thow ... unto] C Thow shalt passe
hens and me come to   109 of this] B, C here of   thow]
not in B   right] not in C   110 shal ... oon] C there
shalle many oon   112 That ... misse] C That yef that
ne were they shuld therof mysse   113 what ... seye]
B, C what here lyked to sey*   114 Shee up to Hevene]
B She to Heven   ascendid up and sty] B, C ascendyd and
stye*   116 as ... Our Lady] B, C as hym told Owre
Ladye*   121 unto] B, C to

54

Who serveth Our Lady leesith right naght.
Shee souffissantly qwytith every deede.
And now, heeraftir the bettre to speede,
125 And in hir grace cheerly for to stonde,
Hir psalteer for to seye let us fonde.

122 leesith] loses   126 fonde] try

---

123 Shee souffissantly] *C* Suffysiantly she
125 for] *B* fort; *not in C*   126 for]
not in C

MS. R.3.21 (ca. 1442–1483),
Trinity College, Cambridge

The Legend of Dan Joos

Text from MS. R.3.21 (ca. 1442-1483; foll. 165ᵇ-167),
Trinity College, Cambridge (*A*); variant readings
from a second copy in the same hand at foll. 236-
237ᵇ (*B*), and from MS. Harley 2,251 (1442-1483;
foll. 70ᵇ-72), British Museum (*C*), which omits lines
92-119. Starred readings are common to *B* and *C*
with minor variations in form.

O welle of swetnesse, replete in every veyne,
That all mankynde preservyd hast from dethe,
And all oure joy fro langour dydest restreyne
At thy nativite; O floure of Nazareth,
5 When the Holygost with hys swete breth
Gan to enspyre the as for hys chosyn place
For love of man by influence of hys grace

And were invyolate; O bryght hevynly sterre
Mong celestynes reynyng without memory,
10 That by thyne empryse in thys mortall werre
Of oure captyvyte gatest the full vyctory:
Whom I beseche, for thyne excellent glory
Som drope of thy grace adowne to me constyll,
In reverence of the thys dyte to fulfyll.

2 That] *subject of* preservyd hast; *Lydgate's pronoun
references are often unclear. Sometimes he omits a pronoun
necessary to the sense: cf. line 8,* were.   9 celestynes]
heavenly beings   without memory] from time immemorial
10 empryse] enterprise   13 constyll] shed   14 dyte]
poem   fulfyll] complete

6 the] *not in C*   8 O] *C* a   12 Whom] *C* Whan

15 That oonely my rewdenes thy myracle nat deface
Whyche whylom sendest in a devoute abbey
Of an hooly monke, thorough thy myght and grace
That of all pyte berest bothe lok and key!
For, benygne Lady, the sothe of thee to sey,
20 Full well thow quytyst that done thee love and serve,
An hundryd sythys bettyr then they deserve,

Ensample of whyche here ys in portreture,
Withoutyn fable, ryght as hit was in dede.
O refuge and welthe to every creature,
25 Thy clerke to further, helpe now at thys nede,
For to my purpose I wyll anone procede:
The trowthe to recorde—I wyll no lengor tary—
Ryght as hit was; a poynt I wyll nat vary.

Vincencius, in hys Speculatyf Historiall,
30 Of thys sayde monke maketh full mensioun
Under the fourme, to yow as I reherse shall,
That by a gardeyne, as he romyd up and doune,
He herde a bysshop of fame and gret renoune
Seying fyve psalmes in honour of that flowre
35 That bare Jhesu Cryst, oure alther redemptowre,

In whyche psalmes, standyng eche in here degre,
Whoso lyst take hede in syngler lettres fyve
Thys blessyd name MARIA there may he se,
That furst of all oure thraldam can depryve
40 To the havon of [deth] when we gan arryve,
And fro the wawes of thys mortall see
Made us to escape from all adversite.

Dystynctly in Latyn here may ye rede echone,
Folowyng these baladys as for youre plesaunce,
45 To whom the bysshop had sayde hys meditacione.
The monke anone delytyd in hys remembraunce,

40 [deth], *supplied from B and C.*

---

20 quytyst] rewardest
21 sythys] times   23 fable] fiction   35 oure alther
redemptowre] the redeemer of us all   36 here] their
degre] order   39 depryve] send away   41 wawes]
waves   44 baladys] stanzas in rhyme royal

---

40 gan arryve] *B, C* gan to arryve*

57

And thought he wold, as for hys most affiaunce,
Cotydyally with hem oonly Oure Lady plese,
That fro all grevaunce hys sorowes myght appese.

50 And therewithall, he wrote hem in hys mynde
So stedfastly with devoute and hy corage
That never a day a worde he foryate behynde,
But seyde hem entyerly into hys last age,
Hys olde gyltes bothe to asoft and swage.
55 Aftyr hyr matyns, as was hys appetyte,
To sey hem ever was hys most delyte.

Therto hys dylygence with all hys hert and myght,
And forthe contynuyd in hys devoutest wyse,
Tyll at last hit befell apon a nyght
60 The hoole covent at mydnyght gan aryse,
As ys her usage, to do to God servyse.
So when they were assemblyd there in generall,
The suppryour, beholdyng aboute over all

As ys hys offyce, that noone of theym were absent,
65 But of Dan Joos he cowde nowyse aspy.
He roose hym up and privyly he went
Into hys chambre, and there he fond hym ly
Deede as a stoone, and lowde he gan cry:
"Helpe," quoth he, "for the love of Oure Lady bryght!
70 Dan Joos, owre brother, ys sodenly dede tonyght!"

The covent anone gan renne halfe in a drede
Tyll they behylde, when passyd was here afray,
Owte of hys mowthe, a roose boothe sprang and sprede,
Fresshe in hys coloure as any floure in May,
75 And other tweyne out of hys eyen gray,
Of hys eares as many full fresshly flowryng
That never yet in gardyne half so feyre gan spryng.

47 affiaunce] trust
48 Cotydyally] Daily   hem] them
54 asoft] mitigate   swage] assuage   55 hyr] their
63 suppryour] subprior   72 afray] fright   75 other
tweyne] two others

---

59 at last] *C* at the last
66 went] *B, C* is went*; *but* ys *has been crossed
out in B.*   68 gan cry] *C* gan to crye   70 dede] *not
in C*   71 in a drede] *C* in dred

Thys rody roose they have so long beholde
That sprang fro hys mowthe, tyll they have espyed
80 Full fayre graven in lettres of bornyd golde
MARIA full curyously, as hit ys specyfyed
In bookes oolde, and anone they have hem hyed
Unto the temple, with lawde and hye solempnyte,
Beryng the corse that all men myght hit se,

85 Whyche they kept in ryalte and hy perfeccioune
Sevyn dayes in the temple, there beyng present,
Tyll thre bysshops of fame and gret renoune
Were comyn thedyr, ryght with devout entent,
And many another clerk with hem by oon assent,
90 To se thys myracle of thys lady bryght,
Seying in thys wyse, with all her hert and myght,

"Lawde, honour, pryce, and hygh reverence
Eternally be to the, O hevynly Juge,
And to thy modyr, that of her gret benyvolence
95 Preserveth from hevynes in thys derke deluge
That doon her magnyfy, and ys her hoole refuge.
More then they serve she quyteth a thowsand folde:
Hyr passyng goodnes of us may nat be tolde."

Thus, when these bysshops and clerkes many oon
100 Had thankyd God as ferforth as they can,
And thys lady that hathe thys grace ydoon,
So full of joy and blysse was every man
Of thys myracle, that syth the world began
Yet herde I never in roundell, prose, ne ryme
105 Of halfe the gladnes that was withyn hem that tyme.

Sone aftyr thys, here jorney gan they holde,
Eche in hys syde, into hys propre place.
Ryght as they fonde overall, so have they tolde
Of thys holy monke. O lady, full of grace,

78 beholde] beheld   80 bornyd]
burnished   92 pryce] praise   95 hevynes] heaviness
97 serve] deserve   98 passyng] surpassing   of us] by us
100 as ferforth as they can] as far as they were able
103 syth] since   107 Eche in hys syde] Each in his own
direction

83 and hye] *not in C*
85 hy] *not in C*   92-119 *not in C*

110 Now well ys hym that can hys hert enbrace
To love the best and chaunge for no new
That art so feythfull thow canst nat be untrew.

O ye fresshe lovers, that lyvyn ever in doublenesse,
And hurt yourself full oft with youre owne knyfe,
115 Your wofull joy ys medlyd ay with byttyrnesse,
Now glad, now sory, now lyte, now pensyfe,
Thus with yourself ye fall ever at stryfe,
Betwene two wawes ay possyd to and fro,
That in contraryosnes ye stryvyn evyr mo.

120 Youre blynde fantasyes now in herte weyve
Of chyldysshe vanyte and let hem overslyde,
And loveth thys lady that can nowyse deceyve,
She ys so stedfast of hert in every syde
That for your nedys so modyrly can provyde;
125 And for your poysy these lettres fyve ye take
Of thys name MARIA, oonly for [hir] sake

That for youre travayle so well woll yow avaunce,
Nat as these wemen on the whyche ye doon delyte,
That fedyn yow all day with feynyd plesaunce
130 Hyd undyr tresoun with many wordys whyte,
But bet then ye deserve she woll yow quyte,
And for ye shall nat labour all in veyne,
Ye shall [have] Heven; there ys no more to seyne.

Whos passyng goodnes may not be comprehendyd
135 In mannys prudence fully to determyne,
She ys so parfyte she cannat be amendyd,
That ay to mercy and pyte doth enclyne.
Now, benygne Lady, that dedyst oure sorowes fyne,
In honour of the that done thy psalmes rede,
140 As was Dan Joos, so quyte hem for theyre mede.

126 [hir], *supplied from C;*
A, B have hys, *but the reference is clearly to the*
Blessed Virgin.   133 [have], *supplied from B, C.*

110 enbrace] hold fast   115 medlyd]
mingled   118 possyd] tossed   120 weyve] empty
125 poysy] poesy   138 fyne] end

111 for] *B* herfore,
or perhaps therfore   124 modyrly] *B, C*
wondyrly*   128 the] *not in C*   139 that done thy
psalmes rede] *C* that these psalmes rede   140 theyre]
B, C hyre*

How the Devil Seduced a Monk

Foll. 70-71

A monke ther was in oon abbay
That clene lyf lyved ay,
Ech day in the mornynge
Bifore alle othere erthely thinge
5   To Oure Lady wolde knele doun
And say with grete devocioun,
"Lady, for thi joies fyve,
Wisse me the redy way on live."
The Devel then envye hade
10 For the prayeres that he made.
He made hym in all manere
As he a faire womman were.
Ech a day he wolde tho
Bifore the monke come and go,
15 That atte laste the monke wes
Gretely tempted in his flesshe.
To the womman his wille he tolde
And asked hir if sche wolde
His paramour in privetee be
20 Outher for catel other for fee.
The Devel then was ful glad
And graunted hym his wille rad.
Aither spake to other thoo

1 oon] an   8 Teach me the right way in life   9 envye]
malice   11 hym] himself   13 Ech a] Every single
tho] then   15 That] So that   19 privetee] secret
20 Either for goods or for pay   22 rad] promptly

Where thai myght her wille do.
25 "In the belle hous," quoth the Devel:
"There we schul be prive and wele.
Under the belle hous in the solere
There schal no man se ne here."
When that forward was made so,
30 Aither yede other fro.
In the morn the monke ros
And byfore Oure Lady gos.
He saide as he was wont to say
Bifore tyme eche day,
35 "Lady, for thi joyes five,
Wisse me the redy way on lyve."
When he hade saide with gode entent,
To the belle hous dore he went;
Longe whyle the dore he soght:
40 For no nede he fond hit noght.
Then forth after about prime,
At Saynt Marie Masse tyme,
The womman come without lette.
In the kirke the monke sche mette.
45 "Monke," sche saide, "How is this?
Thou art not al trewe, ywis."
Quoth the monke witterly,
"At the belle hous I was erly.
I soght about the newe tre:
50 The dore I myght not fynde ne se."
"Monke," sche saide, "I understonde;
At thi matyns thou was so longe."
"Nay," he sayde, "in gode fay,
I saide no thinge today
55 Safe oon orisoun only
Bifore the ymage of Oure Lady."
"Monke," sche saide, "without drede,
Of thine ernde if thou wolt spede,

24 her] their   26 prive and wele] private and well
27 solere] loft   29 forward] promise   30 yede] went
34 Bifore tyme] Early(?); tyme *could also be an error
for* pryme.   40 For no nede] By any means   43 lette]
delay   47 witterly] certainly   53 fay] faith   55 oon]
one   57 drede] doubt   58 ernde] errand   spede]
prosper

62

In the mornynge saye nothinge:
60 Firste do thi likinge;
After saye matyns and masse,
What thou wilt, more or lasse."
The monke thoght on the Develes crafte.
His witt was away rafte.
65 On that other mornynge, he saide noght:
On the womman was al his thoght.
He hyed forth with al his myght:
The dore he fonde anon right.
Withynne the dore proprely
70 Stode the ymage of Oure Lady.
"Monke," sche saide, "how is this?
At this tyme thou gost amysse.
Go ayeyn and clene the schryve;
This is not the redy way of lyve.
75 The wrang way thou art ynne
Of wrecchednesse and of dedly synne."
With that the womman figured was
In the kynde of Sathanas
And vanyssht away right
80 Verreily in many a mannes sight.
The monke then was ful fayn:
Into the kirke he yede ayayn,
And schrofe hym of his mysdede,
And at the laste to Heven he yede.

64 rafte] taken   81 fayn] eager

The Empress of Rome

In Rome another miracle wes,
That bifel by the Emperesse.
The Emperoures brother was a knyght,
And coveited the Emperesse bothe day and nyght.
5 The lady saide ever nay,
Sche wolde not by no way.
When he segh for no nede
Of his ernde he myght not spede,
To the Emperoure then he tolde,
10 And bade hym leve if he wolde,
The Emperesse wolde witterly
Have hade hym to lye hir bye.
The Emperoure anon right
Bade bringe hir of his sight,
15 Without an[y] more respyte
Radly hir h[ed]e of to smyte.

· · · · · · · · · · · · · ·

[The Emperor apparently handed over his wife to
an executioner, who took her into the country and
prepared to carry out his orders.]

· · · · · · · · · · · · · ·

25 A lord with houndes come huntinge
And fond the lady sore wepinge.
He asked then what hir was
And sche tolde hym al the caas.
That lord the tormentour bade
30 Go home ayayn ful rade
And telle the Emperoure in certayn
That he hade the lady slayn.
The knyght toke that faire lady
Home in his companye.
35 A litel bifore, the Emperesse

15-24 *A hole in the MS.*

---

7 for no nede] by any means 8 ernde] mission
spede] prosper 10 leve] believe 11 witterly]
certainly 16 Radly] Quickly 27 what hir
was] what was the matter with her 31 in
certayn] positively

64

Delyvered of a childe wes
And was melche al newe.
Soone after the knyght knewe
That sche was melche in alle wise,
40 He made hir his norice,
And bade hir kepe wele and faire
The childe that schuld be his ayre.
The lady lenged there mekely
And kepte the childe ful clenely.
45 A yomman in the lordes halle
Wowed hir faste with alle,
And ever the lady saide nay,
Nevermore by no way.
When the yomman for no nede
50 Segh that he myght not spede,
To the childe he stele tho
And carfe the throte even atwo.
He tolde the lord in certayn
The norice hade the child slayn.
55 The lord made als faste
Into the see hir to caste,
But by Oure Ladyes grete myght
The wawes helden hir upright
In the see to and fro,
60 That to the grounde sche myght not go.
And at the laste a fisshere segh
Hir floter on the water on hegh,
And into his bote hastily
He toke that faire lady.
65 To the lond he hir broght
And sette hir on the bonke alofte.
When sche was there only,
To Oure Lady sche prayed specialy
To helpe hir in hir grete nede
70 As sche was broght in care and drede.

57 grete, *MS blurred.*   58 helden, *MS blurred.*

37 melche] with milk
40 norice] nurse   43 lenged] stayed   44 kepte]
tended   46 Wowed] Wooed   51 tho] then
55 als faste] as quickly as possible   58 wawes]
waves   62 floter] float   67 only] alone

With that, Oure Lady, by hir myght,
Appered to hir anone right,
And in hir hond an herbe sche broght.
"Emperesse," sche saide, "care thee noght:
75 This herbe thou schalt have.
Al lepre thou schalt save
That knowlechen in open confessioun
Alle the synnes that thai han done.
Go home ayayn to thi cuntre;
80 Thine enemyes schul lepre be.
Thai schal telle in alle manere,
That many a man schal se and here,
Thai that accused thee falsly
In anger and in malencolye.
85 After that thou schalt anon
Hele hem everechone.
So hardily biheete I thee
Thou schalt come to thi degre."
Oure Lady then vanyssht away.
90 Th'Emperesse, for sothe to saye,
In hir hert was ful fayne;
To hir cuntre sche went ayayn.
Sche went [abo]ut fro place to place.

. . . .

[The Empress went about healing lepers. Those who
had brought about her misfortunes had become
lepers, and they came to her to be cured.]

. . . .

105 And after that the [Emper]esse
Tolde hem redy who sche wes.
When the Emperoure segh
That faire miracle that was so hegh
Also done so graciously
110 By the myght of Oure Lady,
And segh the godenesse of his wyf
That so clene hade lad hir lyf

93-105 *A hole in the MS.*

82 That] So that   87 biheete] promise
88 degre] proper estate   91 fayne] eager
106 redy] readily

He toke hir with gode entent.
To the pope with hir he went
115 And of the pope he hade pardoun
Thereas he hade amysse done,
And lyved with hir ful faire ay
Til God toke hem bothe away.

113 entent, *MS blurred.*

Theophilus

Foll. 11-15

Listenyth, bothe grete and smale:
I wil yow tellen a litel tale
Of Tyofle the fre.
Erchedekne he was yplyght,
5 Wyse clerk and a man of myght,
And riche of gold and fee.

Curtes he was and large, ywis,
Festis to maken with men of pris,
And yiftes to yeven.
10 Also he rod on his jolyfte,
He spak al of his dygnete,
How wel that he was threven:

"Ful wel is that ilke man
That welthe hath and wisdam can,
15 In blysse for to leven.
He may the folk wissen and techen,
He may hem helpen and lechen,
He may hem lenen and yeven.

Be myself I it say,

3 fre] noble   4 yplyght] pledged; *some kind of
ecclesiastical investiture is implied.*   6 fee] goods
7 large] lavish   8 pris] worth   9 yiftes to
yeven] to give gifts   10 Also] As   jolyfte]
lightheartedness   14 can] knows   15 leven]
live   16 wissen] instruct   17 lechen] cure
19 Be] Concerning

20 Ther I go in the wey,
    Therof I have gret thought;
    For wysdam I have mekel wele
    Of wordelis good and yiftis fele:
    No thing fayles me nought.

25 Whoso have defaute or nede
    Of good counseil, or of rede,
    Other of gold, othir of fe,
    Cum to me and he schal haven
    Whatsoever he wil craven,
30 For I have gret plente.

    Curteis and large I wil ben
    Whils I leve, so mote I then,
    With word and with dede.
    My rentis ben so gode and fele,
35 Me may nought faylen no wordelis wele
    For no kynes nede.

    Swilk dignete I have nomen
    That I am erchedeken now becomen:
    Tiofle is my name.
40 So large and curteis I schal ben
    Ther is no man that me schal sen
    Of me schal sayn no schame.

    Now wil I walken on my pleyeng.
    Ne dred I nothir duk, ne kyng,
45 Erel, knyght, baron, ne bond.
    Wherso I go, wherso I be,
    Al wordelis blysse folwis me
    In every kynges londe."

    Forth hym wente this clerk, ywis,
50 With mekel joy and mekel blis,
    But in a litel stounde

37 dignete, *MS blurred.*

---

20 Ther] Where   22 wele] wealth
23 wordelis good] worldly
goods   fele] many   26 rede] advice   31 large]
generous   32 then] prosper   36 no kynes]
any kind of   37 Swilk] Such   nomen] acquired
45 bond] serf

Al his wisdam and his good,
Ryght as doth the salte flood,
It sanc doun to grounde.

55 Whan his good was al gon
And he had spendyng non,
Ageynward he hym went,
And as he wente ther allone,
Mekel sorwe he made and mone:
60 Of poverte he hym bement.

"Allas, what schal I don, for schame?
Forsaken I wil my ryght name,
That no man schal me knowe.
Be god I hadde mekel won,
65 And ryght now it is al agon
In a litel throwe.

Mi wisdom is to foly brought,
And al my good is come to nought.
This world chaungeth wel swythe.
70 Men that wer wont unto me louten,
Thei speren hir yates and me therouten:
Therfor I am unblythe.

But now I knowe verely the sode:
This world farith as ebbe and flode;
75 This is mekil wo.
First was I riche, now I am povere.
Now was I sek, and now I covere.
I carful am, ther I go.

Routh me never what I dede
80 Ryght now her in this stede
Richesse for to wynne,

60 bement] bemoaned   64 Be
god] By good *or perhaps* By God   won]
abundance   66 throwe] time   69 wel swythe]
very quickly   70 wont] accustomed   louten]
bow   71 speren hir yates] bar their gates
73 sode] truth(?); *probably a form of* sothe *for
the rhyme*   77 covere] recover   78 carful]
anxious   ther] where   79 Routh me never] It
would not matter to me   80 stede] place

Had I strengthe unto my pay
And my worschip be nyght and day
To holde and to begynne."

85 Ther cam a Jew and herde his mone
As he yede in the wey allone,
And how sore he hym bemente.
For to weten of his care
And tydyng of his hard fare
90 To Tiofle faste he wente.

"Tiofle, whi art thu swilk a wrecche?
And welthe was never thi meche
Of power ne of lore.
Now thu art fallen so lowe
95 Thu may cursen that throwe
That thu ever were bore.

Wel heye on hors thu were wont to ride,
With richesse and with mekil pride,
And now thu gost on fote.
100 Thin art and thin wit it is myswent.
Thourgh pride, I leve, thu art schent.
What thyng is it may ben thi bote?"

Tiofle wex paal of hew,
For he nolde nought the Jew hym knew.
105 Fro hym he wold hym hide.
The Jew perceyved his maner
And yede ever Tiofle ner and ner,
Faste be his syde.

"Tiofle, nothyng schame the.
110 Though thu hidest the fro me
Wel wot I what thu menest.
Say me her thi nede anon:
Therof I schal the bote don
Wel betir than thu wenest."

82-84 If I had enough strength to please me and
to gain and keep my honor by day and by night
86 yede] went   88 weten] know   89 fare]
condition   92-93 There was never your equal in
wealth, power, or learning; And *may be an error
for* Of.   100 myswent] gone astray   102 bote]
remedy

115 "I ne wot what I may sayn.
For schame and sorwe I wolde deyen
Ryght now her in this place.
Gon is al my wordelis good:
Therfor I waxe bothe wilde and wood,
120 For gon is al my grace.

No wonder it is though I sike and care,
For I was wont to noble fare
Among prynces of londes,
And now is al my good awey.
125 I may wel sayn welaway
And wringen bothe myn hondes."

The Jew sey hym so sore mournen,
And thought in herte how he myght hym turnen
To beleven on his lawe.
130 As fayre as he coude,
Neither to stille ne to loude,
He sayde to hym his sawe:

"Tiofle, let thi moanyng chere.
Listne to me and be my fere,
135 And do as I wil the lere.
Yif thu after my wil wilt don,
Thu schalt ben er tomorwen at noon
Richer than thu er were.

I have a lord that hatte Satan.
140 Yif thu wilt becomen his man
He schal the riche man maken.
Gret dignete he schal the yeven
Whils thu on erthe here schal leven,
And gold ynowe the betaken.

145 Therfor bethinke the, I the pray,

127 sey, *MS shows a
mark after* y, *probably a deleted* s.   128 turnen,
crowded and divided at edge of page.

119 wood] mad   121 sike] sigh
127 sey] saw   131 to] too   132 sawe] speech
133 let] stop   chere] behavior   134 fere]
friend   135 lere] teach   139 that hatte Satan]
who is called Satan   144 the betaken] give you

72

Yif thu wilt don as I the say,
Prevely allone;
And I hastely anon
Wil to my maister gon
150 Thin erand for to done."

Tiofle bethoughtte hym sone
What hym was best for to done.
He gan sore siken and murnen.
Whan he had hym al bithought,
155 Hym thoughtte his wisdam halp hym nought.
To the Jew he gan turnen,

And sayd, "Sir, I pray the,
Yif that it thi wil be,
Myn erand that thu wilt bede:
160 To medes he wil yeven me wordely good,
Say hym, I wil with mylde mood
His bond man be in dede.

Go now faste and duel no while.
It were synne to don me gile,
165 For I am ful of care."
"Yis," sayde the Jew, "I wil gon;
Thu schalt sen that I schal don
Belyve a redy fare."

The Jew wente his wey forth
170 Also ryght, as he couthe, north.
Tiofle he leet ther dwellen.
He yede to seken Satanas
That in Helle is and was,
His erand for to tellen.

175 "Satanas, I conjure the
That thu come up and speke with me
As thu beforn hast don:
This day thu schalt have, and I leve,

147 Prevely] Secretly   159 erand] petition
bede] ask   160 To medes] As a reward; *an
if-clause without the conjunction* if   161 mood]
heart   163 duel] delay   168 Belyve] Quickly
fare] journey   178 and I leve] if I live

73

A soule to thi yeres yeve
180 Fro Jesu, Goddis son."

Up he ros, this foule thyng,
As sone as he herde of that tiding:
He rapede hym wel swithe.
Hym thought be the Jewes steven
185 An soule for to drawen fro Heven.
Therfor he was wel blithe.

"Sey me now, thu maister Jew,
What is thi wil I do now?
Thu callest me so yerne:
190 Ister ony thing that I may haven
Or ony good that I may craven?
Telle me swithe, my leve barne."

"Here is a clerk that wisdam can.
For catel he wil becomen thi man.
195 He dredis hym of blame.
He was wont to mekel won
Of wordelis good; now hath he non.
Therof he hath gret schame.

For wordely richesse and of gold and fe
200 He wil yelde hym al to the
With word and with dede."
Satanas sayde, "Yif he wil so,
Sey hym swithe he come me to
And he schal have his mede."

205 Whan Satanas had hym thus red,
The Jew thought he had weel sped
And his erand weel founden.
Ageyn he yede wel swythe,
To maken the clerkis herte blithe
210 That was in gret sorwe bounden.

179 yeres yeve] year's gift   183 rapede]
hastened   184 be] by   steven] voice
189 yerne] eagerly   190 Ister] Is there
192 barne] child   193 can] knows   194 catel]
goods   196 won] abundance   205 red]
counseled   206 sped] prospered   207 founden]
accomplished(?)

74

"Tiofle, I have thin erand don,
And I was to my maister gon.
Cum now, and go we bothe."
Tiofle sayd than, "Is it he yone?
215 I wene he is the Develis sone.
Me begynnis hym to lothe."

The Jew seide, "Hold thu no tale;
Though he be grisly and of hew pale
He is of mekel myght.
220 Of foul semblaunt though he be,
He is bothe large and fre
And a good felawe, I the plyght."

The Jew bad hym he schulde gon
Satanas man to becomen anon:
225 It were hym al to done.
Tiofle stood and sykyd sore.
Lytel he spak; he thoughtte more.
He grauntid hym his bone.

"Fro men I may me nought hide.
230 I may no lenger here abyde,
For I can don no dede.
I am ful of sorwe and wo.
I can nought say what I may do.
Marie, me helpe and rede."

235 Forth wente this careful man
And cam beforn Mayster Satan.
On knes he hym ther sette;
As wel as he couthe,
Neyther stille ne to loude,
240 That meysterlyng he grette:

"Meystir and Syre, wel thu be,
Ther thu sittist in thi se;
I grete the as I can.
Nede hath me so sore taken,

214 yone] yonder   217 Hold
thu no tale] Pay no heed   220 semblaunt]
appearance   225 It was all he needed to do(?)
228 bone] request   239 to] too   242 **Where**
you sit on your throne

245 Myn owen lawe I wil forsaken
And becomen thi man."

"*Bel amy*, wel comen art thu.
Say me thin erand, why and how
That thu art hedir comen to me:
250 I am a mayster and pouste have
Riche to maken ilke povere knave
That wil my servaunt bounden be."

"Maister and Sire, I say it to the,
I was a man of gret dignete,
255 And erchedeken, ywis.
I had richesse and mekil won,
And everydel it is now gon.
Awey is al my blys.

Al mennis cumpany now I fle
260 For schame of my poverte,
And hyde me in hernys allone;
Therfore I am now comen to the.
A riche man yif thu wilt maken me
Servyse I wil the done."

265 "Forsac first Jhesu and Marie,
And al hir hool cumpanye,
With word and with thought,
And make me a charter with thin hond,
As men don that sellen lond,
270 That I lese the nought."

"Sir, I schal wel done thi bone.
The chartre I schal maken sone,
As wel as I can.
Wherso I go or be,
275 Thu may ben seker of me.
I am thi trewe man."

Tyofle made that chartre good,
And wrote it with his owen blood,

245 lawe] religion
247 *Bel amy*] Fair friend   250 pouste] power
257 everydel] completely   261 hernys] corners
270 lese] lose   275 seker] sure

76

And that was al to fele,
280 Swilk sekirnesse to maken
And Jhesu Crist to forsaken
For a litel wele.

Whan the charter wretin was,
And the covenaund mad with Satanas
285 That he myght nought breken,
Satanas thought a long fare
To he was sekir of his ware.
To Tyofle he gan speken:

"I say, clerk, hast thu don thi dede?
290 Art thu redy to taken mede?
Is the chartre good?"
"Sire, the chartre it has no cel.
My trewthe I the plyght, it is mad wel
With myn owen blode."

295 "Red here that chartre anon
Beforn thise men everychon,
That thei moun bere therof witnesse.
In chaffaring of myshappe
Witnesse is good for after-clappe,
300 Be it more or lesse."

The man that wiste of that chaffare,
How the clerk seld hymself for ware,
His herte myghtte sore bleden.
Tyofle gan the chartre taken,
305 As he beforn had it maken,
And tho began he it to reden:

"Alle men knowen that arn and schul ben,
That this chartre schul herin and sen
With eris and with eye,
310 That I, Tyofle, here forsake

279 fele] much
282 wele] prosperity 286 It seemed
to Satan a long business 287 To] Until ware]
property 292 cel] seal 297 moun] may
298 chaffaring] negotiation 299 after-clappe]
adverse consequences 306 tho] then
308 herin] hear

77

God only, and to the Devil me take,
Bothe loude and heye.

For his sylver and his gold,
Lyf and soule I have hym sold
315 To haven withouten ende,
Hym to loven and to serven,
In his servise to levyn and dyen,
Whersoever I wende,

That I schal nought for non nede
320 Fro hym gon in no drede
Be day ne be terme,
But evermore to ben his man
With alle the werkes that I can,
This chartre I wil conferme."

325 Than answerde Satanas,
That foule thyng, ther he was
Beforn him in present;
Whan the chartre was al red,
Hym thoughtte he hadde wel sped;
330 He sayde al his talent:

"The chartre is mad fayre and wel.
I may fynde therin non evyl:
Of betere I have non nede.
Now thu hast the chartre wrought,
335 Thu art myn bothe sold and bought:
Cum now to me and do me manrede!"

Tyofle on his kneis he fel doun tho
Beforn Satanas, with herte wel wo;
He dede it al for nede.
340 "Satanas, I am thi bondeman,
With alle the werkes that I can,
Bothe in word and dede,

To ride or to go, be nyght or be day,
With al the wil that I can or may,
345 And with my wit and my lore,

326 ther] where
330 talent] will   336 manrede] homage
343 be] by

78

Wherso I go or be,
My lord for to holden the
Now and evermore."

A synful dede wroughtte that man
350   Whan he leet God and tok Satan:
He dede it al for nede.
Whan he hadde al don his wil,
As it was bothe lawe and skil,
He yaf the clerk his mede.

355   "For thu so wel hast told thi tale,
Tak the ther pens ful a male:
I schal faylen the nevyr.
Wheder thu ride or go,
Suylk ynowgh and yit mo
360   I schal the fynden evir.

Ryght wel I wille awaunsen the
In that self dygnete
To ben as thu were wone.
Erchedekne I the make.
365   Hors and welthes here I the betake,
And be ever my gode sone.

Wordelis richesse thu schalt have,
What thyng ever thu wilt crave,
And loke thu be trewe.
370   For I have so wel awaunsen the
Loke thu never forsaken me
For no lord newe."

Than sayde Tyofle, "That wil I nought;
It schal never comen in my thought
375   For non kynnis nede.
Wherfor scholde I the forsaken
And anothir lord now taken?
That were a theves dede.

350 leet] left   353 lawe] justice
skil] reason   356 pens ful a male] a bag full of
pennies   359 Suylk] Such   360 fynden]
provide for   361 awaunsen] advance   362 self]
same   363 wone] accustomed   375 For need
of any kind

79

Have good day now, Lord Myn.
380 Body and soule I am thyn,
Evere withouten ende.
Of al my sorwe thu art my leche.
Body and soule I the beteche,
Wherso I ever wende.

385 Alle men may now have joye of me,
Bothe ying and eld whedir he be
That hath me beforn knowen,
That I am now so wel threven:
My lord hath me al this good yeven,
390 For I am al hys owen.

With joye and blysse I may now faren;
I dar myself nevermore caren:
Ryght wel I have spedde.
For to haven here al myn wille,
395 Of wordely good to have my fylle,
My soule is set to wedde.

Good lyf and large I schal leden;
Poverte dar me never dreden,
For nothyng that may befallen:
400 Mi lord wil me don haven
What thyng me list of hym to craven,
Whan I to hym will callen."

And as Tyofle rod, he herde a stevyn,
Iwis it was a voys of Hevyn,
405 That lyghtte adoun to grounde.
A word ther was sayd: "Revertere!"
Whan he it herde, he fel on kne
On swounyng in that stounde.

" 'Revertere! Revertere!'
410 That word, I wot, was sayd of me.
Allas, what have I wrought?

383 beteche] commit   386 ying]
young   391 faren] journey   392 I dar] I need
caren] be troubled   396 wedde] pledge   398 I
need never fear poverty   400 me don haven]
make me have   406 Revertere] Turn back
408 On swounyng] Swooning

80

My richesse I wil lete al gon,
And I forsakes everychon,
For I wil kepen hem nought.

415 Allas, allas, why was I so wod
That I forsok Jhesu so good
That hath bought al mankynne?
I have don the werste dede
That ever ony man dede for nede,
420 And the cursedist synne.

So foul stynkande is my bede
That my prayers may have no stede.
To whom is best that I crye?
Now I have God forsaken
425 Mercy I may never taken
But it be thourgh Marie.

Now mercy, Moder mek and mylde;
A synful clerk fro schame thu schilde
That is in sorwe bounde.
430 Ther was never man so synful in dede
Yif he wil aske the help at nede
Thu herist hym in a stounde.

Now, swete Moder and Lady of grace,
Thu sende me thin help in this place.
435 Thu that art bothe meke and mylde
And ful of merci and of pite,
This day thi grace thu sende me
For Jhesus love that is thi childe,

And for the love of tho harde stoundes
440 That thu haddest of tho woundes
That thi sone sufferd for mannis synne,
And for the teres that thu lete,
Myn synful lyf amende and bete
That I am now inne.

421 bede] prayer
422 stede] profit   423 crye] pray   425 taken]
receive   431 the] of thee   432 Thu herist
hym] You will hear him   442 lete] shed
443 bete] improve

445 And, Lady, for tho joyes fyve
    That thu haddest in thi lyve,
    Moder of Jhesu, thi childe,
    Thu, Lady, that art ful of pite,
    Thi merci this day thu sende me,
450 And fro schame thu me schilde."

    As God it wolde in that stounde,
    The clerk hym fel adoune to the grounde,
    And ther he lay in a suevene.
    Marie, ful of grace, cam
455 For to helpen that careful man,
    Doun fro the blysse of Hevynne.

    "Wak, Tyofle, and slep thu nought,
    For I am comen fro Hevyn loft
    To brynge the good tydynge.
460 Man, why were thu so wod
    That thu forsok my sone good,
    And holdis he alle thynge?

    Al thyng he hath wrought
    With his word and with hys thought:
465 Swilk a lord men scholde taken.
    The Devel of Helle hath nothyng
    But of thefte and false lenyng.
    He is worthy to ben forsaken.

    Yif o man hadde myswrought
470 Alle the synnes that myghtten be thought,
    And he wille them forsaken,
    And sore repente hym of that synne,
    Into that blys my sone is inne
    He schal redly ben taken.

475 What thyng that thu ever hast mysdone,
    Openly or allone,
    Therof drede the nought.
    Yif thu wilt loven me with honur,
    I wil ben thi procatour
480 To hym that hath the wrought."

458 loft] aloft   467 lenyng] inclination
469 o] a   479 procatour] advocate

"Mylde Lady, and Hevyn Quen,
Blissid mote thu ever ben,
For thu hast herd my bone.
Of alle wymmen blyssid thu be,
485 That thin wil is to comen to me
To helpen me thus sone.

I am to the aknowen of this synful dede.
But thu helpe me at this nede
I wot wel I am but lorn.
490 Lady, Queen, thu art ever mylde.
Help me for the love of thi childe
That of the was born.

Lady and Queen, now thu art comen
Doun fro Hevyn yondir aboven
495 To don that is thi wille.
Thu, Lady, unlose me of tho bondes
That I wrot with myn owyn hondes,
And that my soule nought spylle."

"Tyofle, therfore I am comen.
500 Yif thu wilt me serven and loven,
To Helle I schal wende,
And I wille, for the love of the,
Gon to Helle and maken the fre.
The Devel ther schal I schende.

505 Abyd thu me in that stede,
In prayere and in holy bede.
I schal comen ageyn wel sone:
I schal thourgh my sones myght
Bringen the fro that foule wyght,
510 For I have herd thin bone."

Oure Lady tok tho the ryght wey
Into Helle, as I yow say,
Tyofle out to borwen,
Whil Tyofle made hys prayere.

487 I am to the aknowen] I
have confessed to you   488 But] Unless
489 lorn] lost   496 tho] those   498 spylle]
be destroyed   505 Abyd] Await   513 borwen]
redeem

515 It was wel sene he was hir dere;
    Wel aughtte he hir to serven.

    "Blessid be that lady, Hevyn Quen!
    Thourgh hir I hope saved ben
    That is mayden, Marie—
520 Synful wrecche though I be,
    That sche so sone wil helpen me
    Whan I to hir gan krye.

    For nothyng that I have myswrought
    My prayere forsakis sche nought:
525 Hir mercy is ever swete.
    Flour of erthe, Hevyn Quen,
    Blessid mote thu evere ben.
    With love I the grete."

    Anon as Marie to Helle cam,
530 The fend Satan sche undernam
    Of that ilke dede,
    How he thoughtte that mysaventure
    To byen Goddes creature
    For ony kynnis nede.

535 "Satanas, what hast thu ywrought?
    Hast thu my sones best bought
    That he hath bought beforen?
    Satanas, I telle it the,
    Tyofle hath yolden hym to me,
540 And thu hast hym yloren."

    "Certis, therageyn I wille cleymen,
    For that myghtte never befallen
    For non aventure.
    I have a chartre trewe and good.
545 He wrot it hymself with his owen blod.
    Therfor Tyofle is oure."

    "Tyofle, that clerk, ys me wel dere;
    Therfore I am now comen here:
    That chartre I wil haven.

530 undernam] reproved   533 byen]
buy   536 best] creature   539 yolden] yielded
541 cleymen] assert [my] rights

550 Jhesu, my sone, hath hym wroughtte
And sithen on the rode hym boughtte.
With ryght he wil hym craven."

"That chartre thu schalt never wynne,
For it is sperid her withinne.
555 Therto comest thu nought.
For my catel gret plente
Tyofle solde his soule to me,
And I have hym bought."

"That chartre I schal myselvyn taken,
560 And al my wil herein maken,
And care and woo that schal ben thin:
That catel that thu yef the clerk,
It was al of my sones werk;
Therfore he schal be myn."

565 No wondir it was that the fend was wo,
For sche benom hym the chartre tho,
Marie, that lady bryght.
Although he were bothen wroth and grym,
Sche tok the chartre fro under hym
570 And benome hym hys myght.

"Now I wot and now I may telle:
Thi myght is bothen in Heven and in Helle
And overal aboute.
In Helle ne in erthe is no lawe
575 Ne treuthe that is worth an hawe:
My ryght goth alwithoute.

Allas, and wherefore cam thu here—
To reven me of that I boughtte wel dere
And thu thin maysteri her to maken?
580 Why wilt thu, for schame and velenye,
Receyven hym to thi mercye
Whan he hath God forsaken?"

"Satanas, I telle her the:
My sone is so ful of pite

551 sithen] afterward
rode] cross   552 craven] demand
554 sperid] locked   566 benom] took away
578 reven] deprive

585 Whatsoever man hath mysthought,
That he wil have mercy on hem alle
That willen mercy asken and calle,
What man that hath ony thyng myswrought.

I wil here now no lenger dwelle,
590 Ne I wil to the no more telle.
Ayen I wil now wende."
"That ilke tyme I crie welaway
That thu com her this day
My myght doun to schende!"

595 Oure swete Lady wente ayen
Fro Helle, ther sche hadde ben.
Ful wel sche hadde tho sped.
The clerk sche broughtte good tydyng
And a sure tokyn of delyveryng:
600 Sche broughtte hym hom his wed.

"Have now, Tyofle, chartre thin,
And loke thu be ever trewe servaunt myn,
Myn miracles to rede.
Fro the fend I have the brought,
605 Though he beforn had the bought:
Therof dar the nevermore drede.

Yif thu wilt loven wel to serven me,
And my trewe servant ever be,
Than thu schalt saved ben.
610 Go now and do, as I the say,
And I schal wende my wey
Unto Hevyn ageyn."

"Blessid be thu, Lady Myn!
I am ryght glad to ben thyn.
615 Thourgh the I am out-borwen.
My chartre thu hast brought ayen.
Glorious Lady, blessid thu ever ben;
Therfore me nedis nought to sorwen.

Ilke a synful man, now here me.
620 I wil yow sayn wordys thre

591 Ayen] Back   600 wed] contract
606 dar] need   615 out-borwen] ransomed

86

Of Oure Lady Marie,
How I, that hadde Crist Jhesu forsaken,
Redly to hir mercy sche hath me taken
Fro the Fendis balye.

625 Ther may no man ben so synful in thought,
Whatsoevere he hath myswrought,
Good hope and trust he may haven,
That he schal fynde ever mercy
Redly at Oure Lady
630 Yif he wil it of hir craven.

O thu blessid Moder and Lady swete,
With al myn herte I wil the grete
And preysen the among.
I am ever worthy to loven the
635 In Goddis name, and of the
Syngen I wille a song:
'Te Deum laudamus!' "

That lady that gret miracles hath don
For Tyofle, that clerk, on
640 That was nerhand lorn,
Sche brynge us alle to that blys
Ther sche with hir sone ever is,
That was of hir born.

624 balye] stronghold
633 preysen] praise   among] from time to time
640 nerhand] almost

MS. 432
(Early fifteenth century),
Lambeth Palace Library

The Fool of Alexandria

Foll. 85-86

A curatt hadde in his parishe a paryshen rebell, unbuxum and malicious, that did till him many injuriies and harmys, whom the curat blamyd him ofte and wold have amendid him. But forthy that he was hardennyd and evill incorigeble, he cursid him. Sone
5 after that, the curatt died. Whan he was dede, the cursid man repentid him, dreding dampnacion, and habuntdantly weping and sorowing come to the preest and tolde him all the sothe. The preest sent him to the byshop; the byshope sent him to the pope. He went forthe, sorowing and weping. But for he herd tell of an holy
10 hermyte in Egipte, he went to be consaylid of hym. When he had told the hermyte his counseile, the hermyte said, "Iff thou do after my bidding, thou shalt goo to the Fole in Alesaundre, and he shall say the what thou shalt do." The curssid man than beganne to wepe bitterly and said, "Allas that ever I was borne, senne that I
15 may fynde no remedye for my synne!" The hermyte said, "Sonne, wepe nott. He is no fole, as men wenyth, but he is an holy man and a grete clerke. And for the love of God and the Kingdom of Heven he faynyth hym a fole, that he be dispisid in this world and aftir this regne in the tother with Crist; and he lovyth mykkell
20 the Blessid Virgyn Seint Marye, and he is mekill lovyd of herre. I shall write to him for the." He toke a lettir of the hermyte and come to Alexaundre. And ther he sawe the Fole cum into the cite, and many ran after him, casting stonys at hym and many injuriis doing to hym. At evyn, he went from the citee and come to an old

1 paryshen] parishioner   unbuxum] disobedient   2 till] to   3 forthy] because
4 cursid him] had him excommunicated   14 senne] since   20 herre] her

25 chapell. And the cursid man com to hym, weping and sobbyng,
and fell to his feet and gaffe him the letter. Whan he had sene the
letter and wist the cause of his comyng, he fell downe on the erthe
in prayers. And he lying long praying, at the last com Goddis
moder into the chapell and with her many gloriouse virginis, angelis
30 and archangelis, and a multitude of the courte of Heven, and the
chapell shone as the sonnebeme, and the cursid hidde him in a
herne of the chapell for ferdnesse. The Fole roese and toke [t]his
cursid man by the hand and said, "Drede the nought." And
he led hym to Seint Marye and fell down byffore her and prayed
35 her to have mercy on that synffull man, telling her sothe. Than said
she, "Knowist thou him that [the cursid] yf thou saw him?" He
said, "Ye, my Lady." Than she said, "Go seke him, yf thou may
fynd hym in this covent." He sought him and found hym and
brought hym to Goddis moder. Than comaundid she hym to assoyle
40 the cursid man. And whan that was done, the vision passid away,
and he, assoylid, went home with joye.

36 [the cursid], MS *has* thou cursiddist.

---

32 herne] corner   ferdnesse] fear   roese] arose   39 assoyle] absolve

WILLIAM CAXTON
Golden Legend
(Westminster, [1483])

How the Feast of Our Lady's Conception
Was Established

Sigs. m2ᵛ-3

Ancelme, Archebysshop of Caunterburye and pastour of Englond,
sende gretyng and benediction, in Our Lord perpetuel, unto the
bysshops that ben under me, and to alle them that have remembraunce of the Blessyd Vyrgyne Marye, moder of God. Right dere
5 brethren, how the concepcion of the gloryouse Virgyne Marye hath
be shewde somtyme in England, in Fraunce, and in other contreyes
by myracles, I shal reherce to you. In the tyme that it plesed to God
for to correcte the peple of England of theyr evyllys and synnys,
and to constrayne them by hys servyse, he gaf victorye in bataylle to
10 Wylliam, the glorious Duc of Normandye, to wynne and conquere
the Royame of Englond. And after that he was kynge of the londe,
anone, by the helpe of God and of hys prudence, [he] reformed
th'estates and dygnytees of Holy Chyrche into better reformacion
than it had ben. To whyche the Devyl, enemy unto all good werkes,
15 had envye and payned t'empesshe and lette the good werkes as wel
by falsenes of his servauntes as by encombryng of his straungers.
For whan the Danes herde saye that Englond was thus subgette
unto the Normans, anon they made theym redy to withstonde it.
Whan Kynge Wylliam understode this, anon he sente th'Abbot of
20 Ramesey, which was named Helisius, into Denmarke for to knowe
the trouthe. This Abbotte, after that he had don wel and dylygently
the charge of hys commyssion, and that he was retorned a grete

11 Royame] Realm   15 envye] malice   payned t'empesshe] took pains to hinder
lette] stop   16 straungers] foreign neighbors

parte of the see homward, anon aroos a grete tempeste on the see
in suche wyse that the cordes and other habyllemens of the shippe
25 bracke. And the maystres and governours of the shyp, and alle they
that were therin, loste the hope and truste t'escape the peryl of thys
tempest, and alle cryed devoutely to the gloryouse Vyrgyne Marye,
whyche is confoorte to dysconforted and hope to dispayred, and
recomanded themself in the kepyng of God. And anon they sawe
30 comyng tofore the shippe upon the water an honourable persone in
habyte of a bysshop, whiche called the said Abbot in the shyp and
said to hym, "Wylt thou escape thyse peryls of the see and goo
home hole and sauf into thy contre?" And the Abbote answerd,
wepyng, that he desyred that above all other thyng. Thenne said
35 th'aungele to hym, "Knowe thou that I am sente hether by Our
Lady for to saye to the that yf thou wylt here me and doo therafter
thou shalt escape thys peryl of the see." The Abbote promysyd that
gladly he wold obeye to that he shold saye. Thenne said the angele,
"Make covenant to God, and to me, that thou shal do halowe the
40 feste of the concepcion of Our Lady and of her creacion wel and
solempnly, and that thou shalt goo and preche it." And the Abbote
demanded in what tyme thys feste shold be kepte. The aungele
answerd to hym, "The eight[h] day of Decembre." And the Abbot
demaunded hym what offyce and servyse he shold take for the
45 servyse in Holy Chyrche. And the angel answerd, "Alle the Offyce
of the Natyvyte of Our Lady, sauf where thou saist 'natyvyte' thou
shalt saye 'concepcion.'" And anon after, the angel vanysshed away,
and the tempest cessed. And the Abbote cam home saufly into hys
contrey wyth hys companye, and notefyeed to alle them that he
50 myghte that he had herd and seen. And right dere Sirs, yf ye wyl
arryve at the port of helth, late us halowe devoutly the creacion and
the concepcion of the moder of Our Lord, by whom we may
resseyve the reward of her sone in the glorye of Paradys celestial.

43 eight[h], *Caxton has cardinal roman numeral.*

---

24 habyllemens] equipment   33 sauf] safe
39 do halowe] cause to be hallowed   50 that he had herd] that which he had
heard   51 helth] salvation

The Good Knight and His Jealous Wife

Foll. 62-67ᵇ

Lordyngys, curtase and hen[d]e,
Lystyns how this tale schall ende
T[hat] I wyll yow seyne,
And if ye wyll with gode wyll here,
5   Gret gode ye may therin lere
In hert iff ye leyn.

I schall tell wyffe and man
How Owre Lady helpe can
That to hyre clepe at nede;
10   Thare schall no man sykerly
Do nought fore owre dere Lady
Bot he schall have his mede.

Thys schall I preve thorow a skyll.
Herkyns if it be your wyll,
15   Thys gest for to here—
A feyre merakyll of a knyght
And of hys lady, feyre and bryght,
That was hym leffe and dere.

A knyght wonyd here besyde,
20   That had ynoghe of gret pride
Unto hys lyffys ende.

1 hen[d]e] gracious   5 lere] learn   6 iff ye leyn]
if you incline   9 clepe] appeal   10 sykerly] certainly
13 skyll] argument   15 gest] tale   18 leffe] beloved
19 wonyd] dwelt

92

A lady he had to hys wyffe
That he lovyd as hys lyffe,
Was com of nobull kynde.

25 Syche a grace God them gafe
That thei myght no chyld have
Off all a seven yere;
Therefore the knyght and hys lady
Both thei wer full sory
30 And changyd oft ther chere.

Nevertheles, the knyght and hys wyffe
Both thei wer of gowd lyffe.
To God thei made a bone
That he schuld them som chyld send.
35 Jhesu Cryst, that is so hend,
God grantyd them well sone.

So long together thei gan praye
That he sent them childer tweye
Off ther awne blode.
40 The knyght and hys lady wer full blythe,
And thankyd God many a sythe
Off hys sond gode.

Thus the knyght and hys wyfe
Lyved mery in clen lyffe
45 With joy and grete solas,
Tyll sche was with the thyrd chyld.
Well oft thei thankyd Mary myld
That sent them that grace.

Than thei wer both blyth and glad.
50 Iche to other grete joy made,
Both erly and late.
The Devell therof had envy,
And went aboute as a spy,
There trew lufe to abate.

55 Thus dyd the fend, the fowle wyght.
He was about dey and nyght

24 kynde] family   30 chere]
facial expression   33 bone] request   36 God] Good
41 sythe] time   42 sond] sending   52 envy] malice
55 wyght] creature   56 about] actively engaged

In bale to bryng them bothe,
Bot he myght never be the more
In all the tyme ther before
60 Ons to make them wrothe.

Sych a maner had the knyght
In serteyn usage, every nyght
Thorow the longe yere
Into hys chapell for to wend,
65 Before Owre Lady, gode and hend,
To make hys prayere.

Before Oure Lady, suete and dere,
There he made hys prayere
With full gode wyll.
70 Hys lady never ondername
When he yede ne when he cam,
Bot ley and slepyd wyll styll.

The Fend of Hell fondyd fast
Iff that he myght wordys cast
75 For to wrothe them atwyn,
And fore hys wyked intysme[n]t
Well nyghe thei had both be schent:
Herkyns, I schall yow seyn.

Upon a dey, as ye may here,
80 The knyght and his lady dere
Sate in solas,
And ther feyre chylder twey
Went afore them for to pley
In that iche place.

85 The thyrd was in hyre wom, iwys.
The knyght therof had joy and blysse,
And hys lady that stownd.
"Leff Syre," seyd sche,

75 atwyn, *MS has* atywyn.

---

58 *The exact meaning of* be the more *in this context is
uncertain, but the sense seems to be that the Devil was
never able to get the better of them.* 60 Ons] Once
70 ondername] perceived 71 yede] went 72 wyll]
well 73 fondyd] tried 75 atwyn] apart 84 iche]
same

"Lovyst thou anything beter than me
90 That owhere may be fond?"

"Sertys, Dame," he seyd, "nay,
In nothing me nevyn may
I ne have so grete lykyng,
Bot of a woman that I wote
95 I love wele more, God it wote,
Than any erthly thyng."

"Ye, ye," than seyd sche,
"Lovyst thou another better than me?"
And thought a lythere gyn,
100 And wend that hyre lord than
Had lovyd some other woman
In the maner of syne.

Nay, be God, it was not so.
It was an other, worth the two,
105 That he lovyd in lede.
It was Owre Lady that he ment,
And els thei had both be schent
At ther most nede.

The Devyll of Hell wyst wele this,
110 That hyre herte wrethyd is,
And thought it schuld be more.
To Helle he went withouten feyle,
At the fendys to take counseylle
What hym best de were.

115 Thorow counsyll of the fendys felle,
The most schrewys that wer in Helle
Went withouten feyll;
To a wych in the toune thei wente

90 owhere] anywhere   92 me] *indefinite
pronoun*; In nothing me nevyn may: In nothing that can
be named   99 And suspected an evil trick   103 be]
by   105 in lede] among people   110 wrethyd]
angered   113 At] From   114 What it would be best
for him to do; de *is probably an error for* do.   115 felle]
wicked   116 The most schrewys] The greatest shrews

95

That was out of the ryght entent,
120 And told hyre hys counsell:

"Sey, Woman," than seyd he,
"Wyll thou wyne gold and fe?
Hast thou therto nede?
Inowghe I schall the gyfe of tho,
125 That thou of myn erand go
And do als I the rede.

To a castyll I wyll the send,
To the lady gode and hend:
Go thou now forth rathe.
130 Sche is a party of my kyn,
Wherefore I wold with som gyne
Wern hyre of hyre skathe.

Sche is led with grete unryght.
Hyre lord aryseth every nyght
135 And fro hyre goth full styll.
To another woman wendys he,
That he lovys more than such thre,
And pleys with hyre hys fylle.

All cold he comys ayen hyre to.
140 Go to hyre and sey hyre so.
No word thou schalt lye.
The next nyght that schall com
He schall do that he is wone.
Loke that sche aspye!

145 Sey hyre that sche schew hym nought:
So myght sche sone to deth be brought.
Byd hyre lye full styll.

120-156 *The poem has apparently been tampered with,
since the Devil, not the fiends, interviews the witch.
Perhaps* He *should be understood with* went *in line* 117,
and thei *in line* 118 *should be regarded as an error for* ther.
119 entent] frame of mind 122 fe] goods 124 tho]
those 125 If you go on my errand 126 And do as I
tell you 129 rathe] quickly 130 She is a member
of my kin 131 gyne] device 132 Wern] Warn
skathe] injury 136 wendys] goes 143 that he is
wone] that which he is accustomed to do 145 schew]
follow

Iff thou do as I the rede,
Thow schalt have rych mede
150 Of rede gold thy fylle."

"Yis," sche seyd, "well glad am I
For to go to my lady.
I schall be ther full rathe.
Sche hath do me full mykyll gode.
155 I ame full joyfull in my mode
To wern hyre of hyre skathe."

Thorow the Devyllus intysme[n]t
To the castell sche is went,
And salewy[th] the lady ther.
160 "Leffe Madam," seyd sche,
"I wold speke a word with yow
Iff it youre wyll were.

Comly Lady, gent and fre,
I wold the tell a privyte,
165 Iff thou me not bewrye.
Thow schall leve one my lare
Thyng that thow ne wyst are:
Herkyns now, I schall the sey.

Thy lord, that thow lovys so myche,
170 He betrays the sykerlych
And doy[th] the vylony:
He gose fro the iche nyght ons
To a woman in hys wonys.
Luke that thow aspye!

175 The nex nyght that schall com,
He schall do as he is won,
By hyre for to lye;

170 sykerlych] certainly   173 wonys] domain
MS *has* doyht.

155 mode] heart   159 salewy[th]] saluted
163 gent] noble   164 privyte] confidence
165 bewrye] expose   166 leve one my lare] believe
upon my instruction   167 are] previously   168 I
schall the sey] I shall tell you   169 myche] much
170 sykerlych] certainly   173 wonys] domain

97

Bot at thou sew hym nought,
So myght thou sone to deth be broght,
180   Styll that thow lye."

The lady spake wordys no mo.
"Woman," sche seyd, "if it be so
Thow schall have thi mede."
Crystys cursse on ther hedys than,
185   The wych and hyre lorys-man,
Fore that ilke dede!

The fyrst nyght that after cam,
The knyght went to bede anon,
And hys lady dere.
190   Styll sche ley as sche slepe,
Fore that sch[e] wold take kepe
The soth how it were.

Hyre lord wend sche had slepe tho,
And ros up and gan to go,
195   Als he was bowne.
Into his chapell he gan wend,
To pray to Owre Lady hend
That bare Godys son.

When the lady wyst tho
200   That hyre lord was fro hyre go,
Sche sayd, "Alas that whyle!
Now I wote that it is
The wydew seyd me, iwys:
My lord had do me gyle.

205   He lovys another better than me.
Alas, alas!" than seyd sche,
"Myn herte is full of care.
The werke that he wyrkys now,
It schall not fall fore hys prow.
210   It schall hym rew full sore."

178 at] that   sew] follow   184 hedys] heads
185 lorys-man] teacher   191 take kepe] take notice
195 When he was ready   202-203 Now I know that
what the widow told me is true   209 It shall not be to
his advantage

Thus sche gan alon speke,
And thought how [sche] myght it wreke.
To schend hyreselve that tyde,
Sche drew a knyfe, soth to seyn,
215 And slew hyre feyre chylder tweyn
That ley be hyre syde.

When sche had this werke wroght,
Sche seyd, "Alas!" and hyre bethought,
"Myn hert is full of sorow!
220 Wyte my lord what I have don,
He wyll me scle ryght sone,
That no man schall me borow.

Ney, that schall not be so.
Wers I schall myselve do,
225 Whatever therof fall."
With a knyffe, was kene and scherpe,
She smote hyreselve to the herte:
That was werst of all.

Now was this a rewfull syght,
230 In that chamber that same nyght
The man that myght behold:
The lady and hyre chylder twey,
In hyre wombe the thyrd, I sey,
All thei wer wele cold.

235 The Fend of Hell was glad off this,
Fore he wend wele, iwys,
Off them he schuld not feyle.
Bot ye schall here in a whyle
How that he was begyle,
240 And left all hys traveyle.

Fore the knyght, as ye may here,
Ley welle fast in hys prayere
With full gode wylle.
When hys prayers were adone,
245 To hys chamber he went sone,
Hymselve alone, wele stylle.

212 wreke] avenge   213 tyde] time
222 borow] save

99

To the bed the knyght gan go;
He fond hys wyfe, hys chylder two:
Ded thei ley there.
250 The bede was spred with ther blode.
The knyght fore sorow wex ne wode,
And wonderyd on that fare.

"Lady, mersy!" seyd the knyght.
"Who has ben here this nyght
255 And don this rewfull dede?
Lady, helpe! I ame forelorn
Bot ye, that I have ben beforn,
Helpe me at this nede.

Thys woman hath hyreselve schent
260 Thorow the fendys entysme[n]t.
Lord, how may this be?
Iff I be takyn in this lede,
I schall be hangyd fore this dede.
Whether may I fle?

265 Thys castell is so strong withall
I ne mey owte at the wall
Nouwhere aboute,
Tyll tomorn, that it be dey;
Bot I may than skape awey
270 Off my deth I doute."

Thus he wepyd and made wo.
To Owre Lady he clepyd tho:
In herte had he no game.
As he was gyltles of that dede,
275 He preyd here helpe hym in that nede
And scheld hym fro schame.

To the chapell he went in haste
And prayd Oure Lady swyth faste
Send hym of hyre grace.
280 What fore sorow and fore wepe,

251 ne wode] nearly mad   252 on
that fare] at that state of things   262 in this lede]
among these people   264 Whether] Whither   268 that]
when   270 doute] fear   272 tho] then   273 game]
merriment   280 wepe] weeping

Sone he fell fast on sclepe
In that same plas.

Owre Lady foregate hym nothing,
Ne hyre sone, Heven Kyng,
285 To helpe at that nede.
There schall no man, sykyrly,
Do nought fore owre dere Lady
Bot he schall have his mede.

Herkyns how the fendys felle,
290 How that they went oute of Hell,
So lothe thei wer to tyne.
A thousand went on a raw,
Fore thei wend in a throw
The sawle have to pyne.

295 Som were ragyd and long tayled,
Scharpe clawyd and long nayled,
The fendys, every ichon.
Som had hornes grel and long.
Oute of ther mouth the fyre sprong.
300 Withouten lake wer non.

Than this was a grysly syght,
Whoso had sen them that nyght
Com rakyng on a raw.
Lystyns now, and herkyns game,
305 How all ther joy was turnyd to scham
In a lytell throw,

Thorow the myght of Meyd Mary,
That sche com doune from Hevyn hy
Ayene the fendys felle.

286 *MS repeats* no.

---

291 tyne] lose   292 on a raw]
one after another   293 in a throw] in
a short time   294 to pyne] to torment   297 every
ichon] every single one   298 grel] fierce, *or perhaps*
sharp; *probably a form of* gryl   300 lake] fault(?)
301 Than] Then   303 rakyng on a raw] marching in
order   304 game] blithely(?)   308 That] When

310 Sche seyd, "Fendys, fle awey,
Fore here ye have tyned your pray.
The saule schall with me duelle."

"Ney, foresoth," seyd Sathanas,
"Hyte hath hyre happyd a foule cas.
315 Thou feylest of thi arte.
Sche slew hyreselve with myght and onde,
And hyre chylder with hyre hond:
Of them thou hast no parte."

The Quen of Heven stude full styll,
320 And sofyrd them to sey ther wyll.
Thereof sche gan smyle.
"He that lyght in my servys,
It schall be at hys asyse.
He schall not tyn hys whyle."

325 The fendys cryed as thei wer wode,
"Go we hens with body and blode;
No lenger wyll we duelle."
Fowre thousand fendys and one
Wend to take hyre and gone
330 Withoute lettyng to Helle.

"Late be, Fendys, youre feleny.
Wene ye fore to have mastry
At your awne wyll?
Fyrst we schall speke wordys mo
335 That schall yow lyke non of tho
Bot make your hertys gryll.

I congour the, Fend, that thou me sey,
That thou ne lete fore love ne aye,
How came this sorow in place,
340 And in what maner it fyrst began,
Whether that it wer thorow fend or woman:
Tell me, eer thou passe."

316 onde] spite   322 lyght] dwells   323 It] *probably*
an error for I   asyse] judgment   324 tyn hys whyle]
waste his time   330 lettyng] hindrance   335 None of
which shall please you   338 lete] neglect   aye] fear

"Foresoth, Lady," seyd he,
"It com thorow a wych and me:
345 I may it not foresake.
Boldly I have it wrought;
Therefore th[ei] schall to Hell be brought,
There pays for to make."

"Ney, ther me thinke thou doyst wrong
350 When ye hyre chermyd to your hond
That lyved in pese and gryght.
Take ye," sche seyd, "that ye have wrought,
And leve that my sone hath bought,
And delyth no more them wyth.

355 Nay, I yen-sey, sothly.
Whyll sche dyd this foly
Hyre lord was my servant,
And thorow hyre lordys besekyng
They schall have lyfe and gode endyng
360 Thorow my sones grante."

The fendys lowd thei gan crye,
And seyd, "Late be that, Mary!
Hens, I rede thou, fle!
Sche dyd it thorow a myschans,
365 Without schryft and repenta[n]s.
Our sche schall be."

Than ansuerd the Quen, Mary:
"Late be this noys and this cry;
It helpe you ryght nought.
370 Hyre lord and sche be of a blode,
And thorow his werkys trew and gode
To lyfe thei schall be brought,

And ches than at ther fre wyll,
After that they thinke skyll,
375 To whom thei wyll them hold—

347 th[ei], *MS has* thou.

---

348 pays] peace   351 gryght] security; *probably a
form of* gryth *for the rhyme*   355 yen-sey] disagree
366 Our] Ours   370 a blode] one blood   373 ches]
choose   374 According to what they think reasonable

103

With my son for to duell
Or with you, Fendys of Hell,
That makys you so bold."

When the angellus began to se
380 The bodys schuld on lyve be
Thorow Oure Ladys saw,
Every angell a devyll hente
And thyrst them, that there rybbys bent
Fore tene of ther plaw.

385 The fendys saw that they had lorne.
Every fend had other torne
With a mody chere.
Never thei stynte ne blane
To thei to the wych came,
390 And sette hyre house on fyre.

The fyre was blo as brymston.
They brake the wychys bake-bone.
Oneth on lyffe hyre lete.
Hyre neyghbors ther besyde
395 Dorste no lenger abyde,
Bot fled awey full sore.

381 saw] saying   383 thyrst] squeezed   384 tene]
pain   plaw] sport   387 mody] angry   388 stynte]
ceased   blane] stopped   389 To] Until   391 blo]
livid   393 Oneth] Scarcely

NOTES

(Each miracle of the Virgin is summarized only once;
subsequent listings of tales either edited or summarized
are marked with the symbol ‡.)

THE SOUTH ENGLISH LEGENDARY

MS. Harley 2,277, British Museum[1]

The South English Legendary was first edited and published in 1887 by Carl Horstmann, on the basis of the earliest manuscript, MS. Laud 108 (ca. 1280–1290) of the Bodleian Library, which contains only one miracle of the Virgin, "Theophilus" (foll. 127ᵇ-130). Another copy of the same version of "Theophilus," followed by six other miracles of the Virgin, appears in MS. Harley 2,277 (foll. 58-64ᵇ), the second oldest manuscript of *The South English Legendary*. These seven tales are listed and summarized as follows, in the sequence of MS. Harley:

1. "Theophilus": A clerk refused to accept a bishopric, because he felt unworthy. Another was chosen in his stead, who, fearing Theophilus as a rival, took away all his worldly goods and ruined his reputation. Tempted by the Devil, Theophilus sold his soul for the restoration of his worldly dignity. Later, he repented and prayed to the Virgin Mary, who obtained pardon for his sins and forced the Devil to restore the contract which Theophilus had signed.

2. "The Jewish Boy": A Jewish child went into a church with his Christian playmates and received Holy Communion on Easter Day. For this his father wrathfully hurled him into an oven, but he was protected from the fire by the Virgin Mary.

3. "The Devil in Service": Some friars were cast into prison by a wicked knight, whose crimes were caused by the fact that he was haunted by the Devil in the guise of a faithful servant. Despite his wickedness, the knight had a pious custom of saying five "Ave Marias" every day, and the friars were therefore able to gain permission to preach a sermon before the entire household. The Devil was exposed by his failure to attend. He admitted that he would have strangled the knight had he once failed to say his "Aves."

4. "How Our Lady Came to the Devil Instead of the Victim" (here edited).

[1] The best description is that of Beatrice D. Brown, ed. *The Southern Passion*, EETS, Orig. Ser., No. 169 (London, 1927), pp. xvii-xviii.

5. "The Monk Who Could Learn Only 'Ave Maria'": A knight gave up the world and entered a monastery, but he was unable to learn anything except the two words "Ave Maria." After his death, a lily grew from his mouth, bearing upon each leaf the words "Ave Maria."

6. "The Oxford Scholars" (here edited).

7. "Toledo": On the Feast of the Assumption, the voice of the Blessed Virgin startled the worshipers in the Cathedral of Toledo. She complained that the Jews were still allowed to insult her son. Some Jews in the city were caught in the act of wounding a waxen image of Christ.[2]

Another miracle of the Virgin appears in MS. Egerton 2,810 (fourteenth century; fol. 99^b) of the British Museum, also a manuscript of *The South English Legendary* though it contains none of the other tales just enumerated:

"How Our Lady Appeared to a Monk in a Vision": In a certain monastery, during the singing of the "Salve Regina" after compline, a monk saw the Blessed Virgin standing before the altar, bestowing her blessing upon the monastic community.

Since this story is written in short couplets instead of in the septenaries characteristic of *The South English Legendary*, there is some doubt that it actually belongs to that work.[3]

A great deal of controversy surrounds the source of *The South English Legendary*. Some scholars think that it was based on the *Legenda aurea* (ca. 1255) of Jacobus de Voragine,[4] and it is true that a number of the materials, including all of the miracles of the Virgin except "The Oxford Scholars" and "Toledo," appear in that work.[5] But in the present state of the manuscripts, it is not possible to determine the date of *The South English Legendary*,[6] and it seems as likely that both legendaries drew

[2] Editions: (1) Horstmann, *The Early South-English Legendary*, pp. 288-293 (from MS. Laud 108); (2, 3, 5) Tryon, "Miracles of Our Lady," pp. 313-314, 314-316, 319-320; (7) Frederick J. Furnivall, *Early English Poems and Lives of Saints* (Berlin, 1862), pp. 42-43. Tryon also edits (pp. 374-378) other versions of (3) and (5), found together as one poem in MS. Tanner 407 (late fifteenth century; foll. 58^b-59) of the Bodleian Library. Based on the *South English Legendary* poems and similar to them in style, there seems no reason for giving the Tanner material special attention.

[3] Tryon, "Miracles of Our Lady," pp. 320-322 (text), 331 (commentary).

[4] M. E. Wells, "The *South English Legendary* in Its Relation to the *Legenda Aurea*."

[5] Ed. Graesse, Cap. li, *De annunciatione*: "The Monk Who Could Learn Only 'Ave Maria,'" p. 221, and "The Devil in Service," pp. 221-222; Cap. cxix, *De assumptione*: "How Our Lady Came to the Devil Instead of the Victim," pp. 513-514, and "The Jewish Boy," pp. 515-516; Cap. cxxxi, *De nativitate*: "Theophilus," pp. 593-594.

[6] For controversial discussion, see B. D. Brown, pp. xi-xii; M. E. Wells, pp. 339-340.

their contents from related sources. This possibility seems even more probable in view of the fact that those miracles of the Virgin in *The South English Legendary* which occur in the *Legenda aurea* occur also in the *Liber Mariae* (ca. 1300) of Gil de Zamora.[7]

With regard to authorship, nothing definite is known, though numerous theories have been proposed suggesting as possible authors Robert of Gloucester, a team of monks of Gloucester Abbey, one or more friars, and the secular clergy.[8] The place in which the legendary was originally composed has also occasioned dispute, though Gloucestershire and Somersetshire have been proposed most often.[9] The dialect of the oldest manuscripts certainly indicates a West Midland provenience, probably of the southwestern part of that dialect area.[10] Characteristic features of the selections edited here are (1) the third person feminine singular of the personal pronoun in *heo* or *he* (nominative), and *hire* (genitive and objective), and the plural of all genders in *hi* (nom.), *here* (gen.), and *hem* (obj.); (2) the present active indicative of verbs, both the plural forms and the third person singular, in *-th*; (3) the infinitive in *-e*, but *-i* in weak verbs of Old English class II; (4) the present participle in *-inge*; (5) the past participle with the prefix *i-*; (6) the preterit-present form *scholde*: tale 4/line 12; (7) OE *ā* regularly written as *o*: *sore*, tale 4/line 8, *hom*, tale 4/line 21; (8) OE *ȳ* regularly as *u*: *dude*, tale 4/line 8; (9) OE *ĕo* regularly as *u*: *hurte*, tale 6/line 16. There are, of course, exceptions to these generalizations.

How Our Lady Came to the Devil
Instead of the Victim *and*
The Oxford Scholars

Of the tales here edited, only the first occurs in the *Legenda aurea* (Cap. cxix). A slightly different account of the same legend may be

---

[7] Fidel Fita, ed. "Cincuenta leyendas por Gil de Zamora, combinadas con las cantigas de Alfonso Sabio," *Boletin de la Real Academia de la Historia*, VII (1885), 60-68 ("Theophilus"), 68-69 ("The Jewish Boy"), 115-116 ("The Devil in Service"), 131-132 ("How Our Lady Came to the Devil Instead of the Victim"); and Fita, ed. "Treinta leyendas por Gil de Zamora," *Boletin de la Real Academia*, XIII (1888), 191 ("The Monk Who Could Learn Only 'Ave Maria' ").

[8] B. D. Brown, pp. xciii-cx; M. E. Wells, pp. 359-360.

[9] B. D. Brown, pp. xxxi-xxxvi.

[10] For a complete survey of the West Midland dialects, see Mary S. Serjeantson, "The Dialects of the West Midlands in Middle English," *Review of English Studies*, III (1927), 54-67, 186-203, 319-331.

found in eleven manuscripts of *The North English Homily Collection*,[11] but there is no evidence that one was the source of the other.

The second, "The Oxford Scholars," is of unknown origin. Tryon has found an analogue, in which a priest kneeling at the bedside of a dying boy sees the Blessed Virgin bearing his soul to Heaven, in two fourteenth-century Latin manuscripts: one in the Benedictine monastery of Kremsmünster, Austria (MS. 114, item no. 43), the other in the British Museum (Additional MS. 18,346, fol. 69ᵇ).[12] It is interesting to observe that "The Oxford Scholars" appears in all but one of the extant manuscripts which contain the first tale. The exception is MS. Cotton Julius D.ix of the British Museum.

Texts of "How Our Lady Came to the Devil Instead of the Victim" (4) and "The Oxford Scholars" (6).

MSS.: (Asterisk and dagger refer to editions based upon the MSS.)
   Vernon (English Poetry a.1; foll. 55, 56), Bodleian Library
   57 (foll. 53ᵇ, 54ᵇ), Trinity College, Oxford
   Additional 3,039 (foll. 108, 109ᵇ), Cambridge University
   *145 (foll. 87, 88ᵇ), Corpus Christi College, Cambridge
   Pepys 2,344 (pp. 305, 308), Magdalene College, Cambridge
   605 (foll. 246, 247), Trinity College, Cambridge
   Cotton Cleopatra D.ix (foll. 153, 154ᵇ), British Museum
   Cotton Julius D.ix (fol. 302ᵇ), British Museum
   Egerton 2,891 (fol. 96, lines 1-72 only; fol. 97, lines 41-74 only), British Museum
   †Harley 2,277 (foll. 61ᵇ, 63), British Museum
   Additional 10,301 (foll. 101ᵇ-103), British Museum

Editions:

   (4) *Charlotte D'Evelyn and Anna J. Mill, *The South English Legendary*, EETS, Orig. Ser., No. 235 (London, 1956), pp. 231-234.
   †Tryon, "Miracles of Our Lady," pp. 316-319.
   (6) *D'Evelyn and Mill, pp. 235-237.
   †Furnivall, *Early English Poems*, pp. 40-42.

[11] Listed by Carleton F. Brown and Rossell Hope Robbins, *The Index of Middle English Verse* (New York, 1943), p. 258.
[12] "Miracles of Our Lady," p. 330.

THE NORTH ENGLISH HOMILY
COLLECTION

MS. Ch.5.21, Royal College of Physicians, Edinburgh[1]

The North English Homily Collection is a series of discourses on the gospels for Sundays and for certain other days, with *exempla*. It was written ca. 1300, and it is extant in at least three versions, represented by sixteen known manuscripts. The oldest manuscript is Ch.5.21 (fourteenth century; foll. 16-36[b]) of the Royal College of Physicians, Edinburgh. Most scholars place it at the beginning of the fourteenth century, but G. H. Gerould would assign a date near the end. This manuscript is generally considered the best, even though it is a fragment. The prologue as it is there found explains that the homilies are for "lawed men" who do not understand Latin and French. Numerous works have been suggested as the possible source or sources, but there is no evidence in favor of any one in particular.[2]

The homily collection is preceded in the Edinburgh manuscript (foll. 14-15) by the tale of Abbot Elsinus, "How the Feast of Our Lady's Conception Was Established." Similar in style to the other materials, though not actually included among the gospel homilies, this miracle of the Virgin is also found in prose in Caxton's *Golden Legend*, and it is edited from that source in this volume. Apart from this tale, there are four miracles of the Virgin within the gospel homilies, and the manuscript may have contained others originally. The four that have survived are written in rhymed couplets. They are:

1. "The Rule of St. Benedict": A monk whom all considered a holy man died and went to his judgment. When a friend prayed to know the state of his soul, the dead man appeared to him in a vision, explaining that he had been found lacking in devotion to the Rule of St. Benedict and that only his prayers to Our Lady had saved his soul (foll. 20-20[b]).

2. "The Pilgrim of St. James" (here edited).

3. "The Feast of Our Lady's Purification": A woman built a chapel in honor of the Blessed Virgin. On Candlemas, her chaplain being absent, she was unable to have her mass. As she knelt sorrowing

---

[1] Described by Small, ed. *English Metrical Homilies*, pp. xi-xxii. For controversial discussion of the date, see Gordon Hall Gerould, *Saints' Legends* (Boston, 1916), pp. 170-171. For list of MSS, see John Edwin Wells, *A Manual of the Writings in Middle English 1050-1400* (New Haven, 1916), pp. 287-292.

[2] For résumé and bibliography, see James E. Carver, *The Northern Homily Cycle* (New York, 1941), pp. 3-4.

before the altar, she fell asleep and dreamed that she was in a church with a company of people led by a beautiful maiden. Candles were given out, and then Christ himself entered in the vestments of a priest and began to say mass. Led by the maiden, the company rose to offer the candles, but the woman refused to do so, wishing instead to keep hers. Then the maiden, who was really the Virgin Mary, sent a messenger to take it from her by force. When the candle snapped in half, the woman awoke and found that she still held the part that remained in her hand in the dream (foll. 35^b-36).

4. "How an Abbess Was Delivered": An abbess fell into sin. Finding herself with child, she sought the confidence of a younger nun, who reported her to the bishop. When the bishop summoned the abbess to account for her conduct, the woman repented and appealed to Our Lady for help. Our Lady, perceiving the woman's contrition, herself delivered the child and gave it to an angel, who was instructed to give it into the keeping of a hermit. The abbess thereafter lived a pious life (fol. 36^b).[3]

Other manuscripts of *The North English Homily Collection* contain "Theophilus" and "How Our Lady Came to the Devil Instead of the Victim," but the details differ from those in the same legends as they occur in *The South English Legendary*.[4]

The Pilgrim of St. James

"The Pilgrim of St. James" is the eighth tale in Mussafia's *HM* series. There are two versions of the story, both associated with Cluny, and they are extant in numerous variations. In one of the two versions, as found in the third book of *De vita sua* by Guibert de Nogent (d. 1124),[5] the tale is told on the authority of Joffredus de Saumur, whose brother was the famous Abbot Hugh of Cluny. Since the story is not there presented as a miracle of the Virgin, E. F. Wilson notes, "The story . . . illustrates how Mary edged her way into the place of other saints and finally came to occupy the position of importance."[6] This statement, however, may not be true of "The Pilgrim of St. James," for the second of the two versions, the one upon which the unknown poet of *The North English Homily Collection* based his

---

[3] Editions: Small, *English Metrical Homilies*, (1) pp. 29-33, (3-4) pp. 160-171.

[4] For lists see C. F. Brown and Robbins, *The Index of Middle English Verse*, pp. 5, 258. A comparative study of both versions of "Theophilus" is given by Eugen Kölbing, "Die jüngere englische Fassung der Theophilussage," *Englische Studien*, I (1877), 16-57.

[5] In Migne, *Patrologiae*, Ser. Latina, Vol. CLVI (1880), cols. 955-956.

[6] *The Stella maris*, p. 199.

narrative, is at least as old as that given by Guibert de Nogent, and it may be even older.

Southern has traced this second version to a work which he calls *Dicta Anselmi*, written before 1109 and extant in MS. 457 (foll. 77-84) of Corpus Christi College, Cambridge.[7] There it purports to have been told by Abbot Hugh to Anselm of Canterbury during a conference which the two prelates are known to have had at some time between 1099 and 1105. Parts of the *Dicta Anselmi*, including "The Pilgrim of St. James," appear also in a book preserved at Compostella and traditionally ascribed to Calixtus II (pope, 1119-1124). Walter F. Starkie has shown that this so-called *Codex Calixtinus* was probably not written by Pope Calixtus, and he names it more appropriately *The Book of St. James*, dating it ca. 1130.[8] The immediate source of the poem that appears in *The North English Homily Collection* is not known. As for the poem itself, the following forms identify the dialect as Northern: (1) the third person feminine singular of the personal pronoun in *scho* (nom.), and the first person plural of all genders in *thai* (nom.); (2) the third person singular present active indicative (of verbs) in -s: *spekis*, line 20, *demes*, line 81, *bindes*, line 122, *gers*, line 129; (3) the preterit-present form *suld*: line 3; (4) the verb "to be" in *was* for the third person singular and plural preterit indicative; (5) OE *hw* regularly written as *qu*: *Quen*, line 9; (6) OE *c* regularly written as *k*: *mikel*, line 38; (7) OE *ā* regularly unchanged: *sa*, line 5.

Texts of "The Pilgrim of St. James."

MSS.: (Asterisk and dagger refer to editions based upon the MSS.)
  3,440 (fol. 173[b]), Bodleian Library
*Vernon (English Poetry a.1; fol. 170), Bodleian Library
  6,923 (fol. 17), Bodleian Library
  Dd.1.1 (fol. 50), Cambridge University
  Gg.5.31 (fol. 21), Cambridge University
  Harley 2,391 (fol. 229), British Museum
  Additional 28,010 (fol. 16), British Museum
†Ch.5.21 (fol. 23[b]), Royal College of Physicians, Edinburgh
  Bute (p. 25), private collection of the Marquess of Bute
  260 (fol. 7), Lambeth Palace Library
  HM 129 (fol. 8), Huntington Library

[7] "The English Origins," p. 189.
[8] *The Road to Santiago* (New York, 1957), p. 1.

Editions:

*Horstmann, "Die Evangelien-Geschichten der Homiliensammlung des Ms. Vernon," *Archiv für das Studium der neueren Sprachen und Literaturen*, LVII (1877), 245-246.

†Small, *English Metrical Homilies*, pp. 53-59.

MS. AUCHINLECK

(Advocates MS. 19.2.1),

National Library of Scotland[1]

The Clerk Who Would See Our Lady

There are two miracles of the Virgin in this famous miscellany. The first (foll. 37^b-38^b) is the one edited here. It is acephalous, because the leaf on which it begins has been cut away, leaving part of the second column on the stub, with the beginnings of the lines mutilated. This part of the poem has been emended in the only edition, that of Horstmann, on the basis of the rest of the manuscript.[2] An occasional letter that appears in the manuscript as a stump or else as an ambiguous letter is not so identified in Horstmann's edition.

There is a prose synopsis of this miracle of the Virgin in John Mirk's *Festial*, a *liber festivalis* written in Shropshire ca. 1415,[3] but it gives no details that would augment those in the Auchinleck poem, and its source is not known. A somewhat different version of the tale, in Latin, may be found in Additional MS. 33,956 (early fourteenth century; fol. 74) of the British Museum, where the vision is granted to an abbot. Still another version occurs in a copy of Herolt's "Promptuarium de miraculis," found in Additional MS. 19,909 (1473; fol. 248^b) of the British Museum. The source of the Auchinleck poem is not known, though Laura H. Loomis has established that the manuscript was copied in London.[4] The dialect of the poem has features which are Midland and also some which are Southern: (1) the third person

---

[1] The best descriptions are those of Kölbing, "Vier Romanzen-Handschriften," *Englische Studien*, VII (1884), 177-191, and Laura Hibbard Loomis, "The Auchinleck Manuscript and a Possible London Bookshop of 1330-1340," *PMLA*, LVII (1942), 595-627.

[2] *Altenglische Legenden*, pp. 499-502.

[3] Edited by Theodor Erbe, *Mirk's Festial: A Collection of Homilies*, EETS, Extra Ser., No. 96 (London, 1905), pp. 234-235.

[4] "The Auchinleck Manuscript and a Possible London Bookshop."

singular feminine of the personal pronoun in *sche* or *hye* (nom.), *hir* (gen. and obj.); (2) the third person singular present active indicative (of verbs) in *-eth*; (3) the infinitive in *-n*, except weak verbs of OE class II, regularly ending in *-i*; (4) the past participle in *-n*, usually accompanied by the prefix *i-* or *y-*; (5) OE *ā* regularly written as *o*: *sore*, line 86; (6) OE *ȳ* regularly as *i*: *Michel*, line 119.

The second miracle of the Virgin (foll. 259-260ᵇ) is a copy of the poem in MS. Digby 86, "Coment le sauter Noustre Dame fu primes cuntrové" (no title is given in MS. Auchinleck), which has been discussed in the Introduction as one of the earliest miracles of the Virgin extant in Middle English. A summary follows:

> A young man whose father had taught him to say fifty "Ave Marias" every day retained this custom when he became a monk. Our Lady appeared to him, clad in an unfinished garment. She explained that his prayers had woven her garment but that he would have to finish it by increasing his "Ave Marias" to a hundred and fifty. The monk did this, and soon afterward she appeared again and showed him that her garment was finished.

This poem has considerable interest for us because Hoccleve's miracle of the Virgin (edited in this volume) deals with the same story, and because the Auchinleck manuscript has been connected with Chaucer (by L. H. Loomis) on the basis of the probability that his "Sir Thopas" is a satire of its metrical romances, such as "Guy of Warwick."[5] If Chaucer knew the manuscript, as seems likely, it is not improbable that Hoccleve saw it as well and that he found there the source of his miracle of the Virgin.

MS. VERNON

(MS. English Poetry a.1), *Bodleian Library*[1]

MS. Vernon, which scholars have placed at various dates between 1370 and 1400,[2] is best known for its A text of *Piers Plowman*. Discussion of the manuscript and of its contents is made difficult by errors in

---

[5] "Chaucer and the Auchinleck MS: 'Thopas' and 'Guy of Warwick,'" in *Essays and Studies in Honor of Carleton Brown* (New York, 1940), pp. 111-128.

[1] The best descriptions are those of Serjeantson, "The Index of the Vernon Manuscript," *Modern Language Review*, XXXII (1937), 222-224, and George Kane, ed. *Piers Plowman: The A Version* (London, 1960), p. 17.

[2] Kane, p. 17.

the foliation, which also show in the index. Other important contents of the manuscript are versions of *The South English Legendary* and of *The North English Homily Collection*. The remains of a *mariale* occupy foll. 123ᵇ-126. Since the foliation occurs upper left *verso* instead of upper right *recto* which is more common among manuscripts, the present edition follows Mary S. Serjeantson in using the symbol ᵇ for the right-hand page of the open book. According to the index, the *mariale* once contained forty-two miracles of the Virgin, but it now ends in the middle of the ninth tale due to the loss of some leaves. Each of the nine is accompanied by an illuminated illustration. The legends now extant are the following:

1. "How Chartres Was Saved" (here edited).
2. "The Child Slain by Jews" (here edited).
3. "The Harlot's Prayer": In Rome, there was a prostitute who tried to tempt a hermit to sin. When he meekly replied to her wiles by confessing his sins and saying that he would pray for her, the harlot declared that she had no need of his prayers. Then he begged her to pray for him. The next time she passed a church, she remembered this and knelt before an image of the Virgin and her child in order to pray. Thereupon, Our Lady asked her child to forgive the harlot, who was converted at once from her sins.
4. "The Jewish Boy" (here edited).
5. "How Our Lady Restored a Man's Leg": A man's leg was so badly inflamed that nothing would cure it. Growing weary of praying for cure without avail, he had it cut off. Our Lady then appeared to him in a vision and restored his leg.
6. "The Merchant's Surety" (here edited).
7. "The Priest Who Sinned with a Nun": A priest who had sinned with a nun refused to make his confession until the hour of his death. He then made confession to a priest who was a friend of his. This priest promised to pray for his soul. A year later, when he was saying his mass, the Blessed Virgin stood by him and revealed the soul of the dead man, cleansed from sin and waiting to receive Holy Communion from him.
8. "How Our Lady's Milk Healed a Monk's Throat": The Blessed Virgin appeared to a man who was dying of quinsy and healed him with milk from her breast.
9. "The Drowned Sacristan": A sacristan, who prayed to Our Lady every day despite an otherwise sinful life, drowned on the way to

visit his mistress. His soul was restored to his body by Our Lady's intercession in order that he might do penance for his sins.[3]

These miracles of the Virgin are written in rhymed couplets of four stresses, except the eighth tale (rhymed a b a b) and the ninth (in rhymed septenaries). There was probably considerable metrical variation in the original *mariale*.

Serjeantson's study of the dialect of MS. Vernon has established its provenience as West Midland,[4] and the most recent discussion of the manuscript, that of George Kane, accepts her identification of South Shropshire–South Staffordshire as the particular area in which it was copied. The dialect of the selections from the *mariale* here edited shows the following characteristics: (1) the third person singular feminine of the personal pronoun in *heo* (nom.) and *hire* (gen., obj.), and the plural of all genders in *thei* (nom.), *heore* (gen.), *heom* (obj.); (2) the plural of verbs, and the third person singular present active indicative, in *-th*, though a plural in *-es* occurs in tale 6/line 5: *telles*; (3) the present participle in *-yng*; (4) the past participle in *-n*, usually accompanied by the prefix *i-* or *y-*; (5) OE *ā* regularly written as *o*: *holi*, tale 1/line 43; (6) OE *ă* before a nasal as either *o* or *a*: *con*, tale 1/line 12, *can*, tale 1/line 13; (7) OE *y̆* regularly as *u*: *lusten*, tale 1/line 1; (8) initial *f* occasionally as *v*: *vengen*, tale 4/line 74.

How Chartres Was Saved[5]

The story of Bishop Waltelin's victory over Rollo and his Norsemen is recorded by the chronicler William of Jumièges in the second half of the twelfth century. According to him, Richard, Duke of Burgundy, rushed upon the Norsemen while the Bishop of Chartres (William calls him Antelmus) attacked from behind carrying Our Lady's relic aloft as a standard. When Ebalus, Count of Poitiers, arrived to reinforce the men of Chartres, Rollo fled in the night.[6]

The author of the Vernon narrative says of his source, "Of Bruit the Cronicle witnesset wel / This conquest of Rollo everidel." But the event is not found in the chronicles of that name written by Wace and Layamon. The reference is perhaps intended to be to Wace's *Roman*

---

[3] Editions: Horstmann, *The Minor Poems of the Vernon MS.*, Part I, EETS, Orig. Ser., No. 98 (London, 1892), (3) pp. 145-149, (5) pp. 154-157, (7-9) pp. 162-167.

[4] "The Index of the Vernon Manuscript."

[5] Edited by Horstmann in *The Minor Poems of the Vernon MS.*, I, pp. 138-141.

[6] *Gesta Normannorum ducum*, ed. Jean Marx (Rouen, 1914), pp. 26-27.

de Rou, written ca. 1160.[7] It cannot be shown, however, that the *Roman de Rou* was the Vernon poet's immediate source.

In her study of the tale as it appears in the *Stella maris* of John of Garland, Wilson (p. 187) shows how the miraculous element in the story came to be stressed at the expense of the Duke of Burgundy and the Count of Poitiers. In the account of the legend given among the miracles of Chartres, for example, the enemy are blinded when they look upon the relic.[8] William of Malmesbury gives substantially the same details, but he does not mention the reinforcements which arrived in time to assist the men of Chartres.[9]

The Child Slain by Jews[10]

Of all the analogues of the "Prioress's Tale," this one bears the closest resemblance to Chaucer's miracle of the Virgin. In 1910, Carleton Brown's interest in the legend led to the collection and study of twenty-six of its variants, widely distributed among the languages of western Europe.[11] With the aid of these variants, we can see that this miracle of the Virgin was a familiar one and that, whatever Chaucer's immediate source may have been, his intended audience probably knew the story in advance.

The Vernon poem has attracted more attention as the possible source of the "Prioress's Tale" than it has attracted as a piece of literature in its own right. Brown, on the basis of differences in detail, rejected the possibility that Chaucer used it as his source,[12] and recent tendency to place the manuscript closer to 1400 than to the earlier dates that have been suggested brings it very near to the date now assigned to the "Prioress's Tale" (the last decade of the fourteenth century),[13] and this decreases the possibility that it was available to Chaucer. There is likewise no information that would identify the source of the Vernon poem.

The Vernon poem does not have the liturgical coloring of the

---

[7] Edited by Hugo Andresen, *Maistre Wace's Roman de Rou et des ducs de Normandie*, I (Heilbronn, 1877), 68-71.

[8] Antoine Thomas, "Les miracles de Notre-Dame de Chartres," *Bibliothèque de l'Ecole des chartes*, XLII (1881), 549-550.

[9] *De gestis regum Anglorum*, ed. William Stubbs, Rerum Britannicarum Medii Aevi Scriptores, No. 90, Vol. I (London, 1887), 137-138.

[10] Edited by Horstmann in *The Minor Poems of the Vernon MS.*, I, pp. 141-145.

[11] *A Study of the Miracle of Our Lady Told by Chaucer's Prioress*, Chaucer Soc., 2nd Ser., No. 45 (London), pp. 1-50.

[12] Ibid., p. 112.

[13] Fred N. Robinson, *The Works of Geoffrey Chaucer*, 2nd ed. (Boston, 1957), pp. xxix, 734.

"Prioress's Tale," and the child singer has a more practical purpose for his fatal song than Chaucer gives him. The song itself may be more important to the murder that follows than scholars have supposed, and it is interesting to observe that there is some inconsistency among the various analogues in this regard. Most of the older ones cite as the hymn the *responsorium* "Gaude Maria," some singling out in particular the words "Erubescat Judaeus infelix, qui dicit Christum Joseph semine esse natum" as the child's song.[14] These words could be interpreted as anti-Semitic, and offensive enough to suggest the original motive for the crime. Since a text of the "Gaude Maria" appears without the "Erubescat" in J. Wickham Legg's edition of the Sarum Missal,[15] it is evident that the *responsorium* was not universally accompanied by these words, and without them the "Gaude Maria" ceases to be necessary to the story. This circumstance may explain how other hymns came to be associated with the story, and it may also explain the real reason why the child is slain for his song.

Much speculation has been occasioned by the mysterious "greyn" that appears in the mouth of Chaucer's little clergeon, causing him to sing after his throat has been cut. The Vernon poem has a similar motif: the bishop, seeking the cause of the singing, finds a lily in the child's throat. The Vernon poet, however, spoils the significance of the lily as the cause of the singing, for, after saying that the singing stops following its removal, he has the child sit up and sing at his funeral. Exactly what Chaucer meant by "greyn" in his account of the miracle we do not know,[16] but there is certainly some connection between that and the lily of the Vernon story, and between both tales and a series of miracles of the Virgin in which a sign appears in the mouth of a person who has prayed faithfully to Our Lady. Since Lydgate's "The Legend of Dan Joos" deals with one of these tales, the subject will be discussed in connection with his poem.

The Jewish Boy[17]

"The Jewish Boy" is one of the oldest of the miracles of the Virgin. It is first found in the writings of the Greek historian Evragius Scholasticus (d. ca. 594), whose account of the miracle may be summarized as follows:

---

[14] The whole text is printed by C. F. Brown, *A Study of the Miracle*, p. 71.
[15] *The Sarum Missal* (Oxford, 1916), p. 496.
[16] Robinson, p. 736, n. 662, gives a bibliography on this point.
[17] Edited by Horstmann in *The Minor Poems of the Vernon MS.*, I, pp. 149-154.

A Jewish glassblower's son, who attended a school where there were Christian boys, partook of some leftover Communion bread, which by custom was distributed to school children. When the child's father heard of this, he hurled him into his furnace, where the Blessed Virgin protected him from harm. The Jewish father was afterward crucified by order of Justinian.

This and thirty-two other analogues of the legend, in Greek, Latin, French, Spanish, and several non-European languages, have been edited and discussed by Eugen Wolter, whose study of the tale is the authoritative one.[18] In one of these analogues, translated into Latin from a Greek source by Johannes Monachus in the ninth century, the child is baptized by his playmates, and his angry parents hand him over to the keeper of a bath, who is ordered to burn him in the furnace.[19]

The version of the tale here edited occurs in Mussafia's *Elements* series, where it is localized in the city of Bourges and told by Peter, a monk of Chiusa,[20] and it is also found in the Harley text of *The South English Legendary* (fol. 60ᵇ). An excellent study of the tale, with bibliography, is given by Wilson.[21]

The Merchant's Surety[22]

This story was translated into Latin from a ninth-century Greek sermon by Johannes Monachus, but there is no evidence that his redaction was the first to appear in Latin. In his account, the Jew is a friend of the merchant Theodore, and he denies receiving his payment in order to test the power of Christianity. The surety is a crucifix, so it would seem that the tale was not originally a miracle of the Virgin. Theodore's silver is used to decorate the Church of Santa Sophia.[23]

Wilson has found four analogues of this miracle of the Virgin. In addition to the one just described, there is another in which a peddler gives an image of Our Lady to the Jew as security for a loan, and upon his return he puts the payment into a bag which he hangs around the neck of the image. When the Jew denies receiving the money, the statue reveals the truth to some onlookers. A third analogue gives the tale a

18 *Der Judenknabe* (Halle, 1879). The analogue here summarized is edited on pp. 28-29.

19 *Liber de miraculis*, ed. P. Michael Huber, Sammlung mittellateinischer Texte, No. 7 (Heidelberg, 1913), pp. 46-49.

20 For discussion, see Southern, "The English Origins," pp. 191-192.

21 *The Stella maris*, pp. 157-159.

22 Edited by Horstmann in *The Minor Poems of the Vernon MS.*, I, pp. 157-161.

23 *Liber de miraculis*, ed. Huber, p. 35.

frame, in which the miracle is told to an archdeacon visiting the scene of the events described. The fourth is the one given in the Vernon *mariale*; this also occurs in Additional MS. 39,996 of the British Museum.[24]

THOMAS HOCCLEVE

HM 744, *Huntington Library*

The Monk and Our Lady's Sleeves

"The Monk and Our Lady's Sleeves" is a form of the miracle of the Virgin which appears in MS. Digby 86 under the title "Coment le sauter Noustre Dame fu primes cuntrové," and which appears also in MS. Auchinleck. The story has not been found in Latin or in French, but some version of it probably occurred in the missing section of the Vernon *mariale*, for the index lists as the twentieth entry, "Hou Ure Lady sauter bygan." Laura H. Loomis has established that MS. Auchinleck was copied in London and that Chaucer was probably familiar with it because some of its tail-rhyme romances can be connected with "Sir Thopas."[1] It is not impossible that Hoccleve knew the Vernon *mariale*, though there is no evidence that it was the source of his miracle of the Virgin.

Of the three manuscripts in which Hoccleve's poem is extant, the earliest and the best is HM 744 (early fifteenth century; foll. 36-39^b) of the Huntington Library.[2] This is a matter of some importance, because paleographical evidence has been found, by Herbert C. Schulz of the Huntington Library, that the manuscript has come down to us in Hoccleve's own hand.[3] Of the other two manuscripts containing the poem, MS. 152 (1460-1500) of Christ Church College, Oxford, is the more important because it is a manuscript of the *Canterbury Tales*.[4] Here, however, Hoccleve's miracle of the Virgin (foll. 229-231) is offered

---

[24] Wilson, ed. *The Stella maris*, pp. 173-175.

[1] "The Auchinleck Manuscript and a Possible London Bookshop," and "Chaucer and the Auchinleck MS."

[2] Described by Seymour de Ricci and William Jerome Wilson, *Census of Medieval and Renaissance Manuscripts in the United States and Canada*, I (New York, 1935), 74. This manuscript was formerly known as Ashburnham Additional MS. 133 and as MS. Gollancz.

[3] "Thomas Hoccleve, Scribe," *Speculum*, XII (1937), 71-76.

[4] Described by John Matthews Manly and Edith Rickert, *The Text of the Canterbury Tales* (Chicago, 1940), I, 85-91.

as the "Ploughman's Tale," inserted between the "Squire's Tale" and the "Second Nun's Tale" by means of a link in no way resembling Chaucer's literary style. This intrusion can hardly fail to surround the Christ Church copy of Hoccleve's poem with suspicion that it may have been tampered with in other ways, and for this reason its variant readings present a problem, especially since some of them supply readings which appear to be better than the ones in HM 744.

The problem becomes more interesting with the discovery that the third copy of Hoccleve's poem, in MS. R.3.21 (ca. 1442-1483; foll. 274^b-275^b) of Trinity College, Cambridge,[5] slightly older than the Christ Church manuscript, gives some of the same variant readings, while at the same time containing variants of its own. Except for minutiae of spelling and capitalization, which have not been recorded, the deviations from HM 744 may be examined in footnotes of the present edition. Comparison shows that there must have been a revision of "The Monk and Our Lady's Sleeves" containing changes in the poem made by Hoccleve himself or by someone else and that the Christ Church and Trinity College copies of the poem are probably mutually independent and based upon this revision. Moreover, a study of the Trinity College copy shows considerable inferiority to the Christ Church copy. Aside from the fact that the scribe has left out line 82, the really important weakness is the fact that some of the variant readings destroy the meter. It seems, then, that the Christ Church manuscript offers the best extant copy of a revision of Hoccleve's miracle of the Virgin. However, the likelihood that HM 744 is a holograph suggests that it is the best manuscript containing the poem.

This brings us to the poem itself, here edited from HM 744. The manuscript contains ten of Hoccleve's minor poems, preceded by a calendar and by a religious tract in prose from which the ending has been lost. The evidence for Schulz's opinion that the manuscript is in Hoccleve's own handwriting is based on the poet's career as clerk of the Privy Seal and on the assumption that an author so employed would be likely to carry into the copying of his literary works writing habits characteristic of court or business hand. There is no dearth of material from which to study the handwriting of the manuscript under consideration, for there are two other manuscripts which are thought to be in Hoccleve's handwriting. One is HM 111, another collection of the poet's literary works, also in the Huntington Library. The other is a volume of documents in French, Latin, and English that passed

---

[5] Described by Montague Rhodes James, *The Western Manuscripts in the Library of Trinity College, Cambridge*, II (Cambridge, 1901), 83-95.

under the Privy Seal (Additional MS. 24,062 of the British Museum). This manuscript, written in court hand, bears the marginal note (fol. 101[b]), "Hic finitur calendera istius libri secundum composicionem Thome Hoclyf. Facta per manum suam ad finem libri." According to Schulz, all these manuscripts contain characteristic letter formations belonging to the same scribe, namely Hoccleve.

Up to the present time, there have been two editions of the text under consideration: that of Arthur Beatty,[6] which also contains an edition of the Christ Church text, and that of Sir Israel Gollancz,[7] certainly the more accurate edition of the two. Comments on the manuscript and on the transcriptions represented by Beatty's edition may be found in J. H. Kern's article "Een en ander over Thomas Hoccleve en zijn Werken," which has unfortunately not been translated.[8] Other comments may be found in F. J. Furnivall's introduction to his edition of Hoccleve's works.[9] There is brief comment on the legend itself in Beatty's introduction, but the information in his discussion of its background is not accurate and has been the subject of a more recent study.[10]

"The Monk and Our Lady's Sleeves" deals with a form of worship known in the Middle Ages as Our Lady's Psalter and in modern times as the Rosary. Our Lady's Psalter was the recitation of "Ave Marias" in multiples of one hundred and fifty, the number of psalms in the Psalter. This procedure had its origin in the monasteries, where there were many illiterate lay brothers who were nevertheless under the monastic obligation of taking part in the Divine Office. The custom of giving them numbers of "Pater nosters" and "Ave Marias" to say instead spread outside the monasteries and became a common form of worship eventually standardized in its present form. The story told by the author of the Digby-Auchinleck poem and retold by Hoccleve was evidently intended to teach what someone believed to be the correct way to say Our Lady's Psalter. The two poems differ slightly in that the older one does not mention "Pater nosters."

Hoccleve may have written this miracle of the Virgin for a patron, since HM 744 bears the marginal note (fol. 36), "Ce feust faite a

[6] *A New Ploughman's Tale: Thomas Hoccleve's Legend of the Virgin and Her Sleeveless Garment*, Chaucer Soc., 2nd Ser., No. 34 (London, 1902).

[7] *Hoccleve's Works*, II, *The Minor Poems in the Ashburnham MS. Addit. 133*, EETS, Extra Ser., No. 73 (London, 1925), pp. 15-19.

[8] *Verslagen en Mededeelingen der Koninklijke Akademie van Wetenschappen*, Reeks 5, Deel I (1915), 365-390.

[9] *Hoccleve's Works*, I, *The Minor Poems in the Phillipps MS. 8151 (Cheltenham) and the Durham MS. III. 9*, EETS, Extra Ser., No. 61 (London, 1892), pp. xxvii-xxix.

[10] See my "Hoccleve's Miracle of the Virgin," *Texas Studies in English*, XXXV (1956), 116-122.

linstance de T. Marleburgh." The identity of T. Marleburgh is not known. From a literary point of view, the poem compares favorably with Hoccleve's best writing, though it is strongly under the influence of Chaucer's style.

JOHN LYDGATE

MS. R.3.21, *Trinity College, Cambridge*

The Legend of Dan Joos

Lydgate's only miracle of the Virgin has come down to us in three copies. Two of them, in the same hand, are in MS. R.3.21 (ca. 1442-1483; foll. 165[b]-167, and foll. 236-237[b]) of Trinity College, Cambridge.[1] The other is in MS. Harley 2,251 (1442-1483; foll. 70[b]-72) of the British Museum.[2] Both manuscripts are collections of miscellaneous poems, apparently copied in the form of fascicles intended for separate use and later bound together in their present form. Both were probably the work of John Shirley's associates.[3]

John Bale, who in 1548 set up the first canon of Lydgate's works, did not include "The Legend of Dan Joos."[4] Not until Joseph Ritson's Lydgate canon of 1802 was this miracle of the Virgin listed among Lydgate's poems.[5] Since that year, the poem has been edited for the Percy Society by James O. Halliwell,[6] for the Chaucer Society by Horstmann,[7] and for the Early English Text Society by Henry N.

---

[1] Described by James, *The Western Manuscripts*, II, 83-95.

[2] Described by Manly and Rickert, I, 241-244.

[3] Eleanor Prescott Hammond, "A Scribe of Chaucer," *Modern Philology*, XXVII (1929-30), 27; and Hammond, "Two British Museum Manuscripts. (Harley 2251 and Adds. 34360.) A Contribution to the Bibliography of John Lydgate," *Anglia*, XXVIII (1905), 1-28.

[4] Bale's bibliography of famous authors was printed first at Ipswich and afterward (1549) at Wesel with changes in the title page. It was revised and issued at Basel as two volumes (1557 and 1559). It is in the Basel version that the work is best known, under the title *Scriptorum illustrium Maioris Brytannie, quam nunc Angliam & Scotiam vocant: Catalogus*. The Lydgate canon appears on pp. 228-231 of the edition by Reginald Lane Poole and Mary Bateson, *Index Britanniae scriptorum* (Oxford, 1902).

[5] *Bibliographia poetica* (London), pp. 66-87.

[6] *A Selection from the Minor Poems of Dan John Lydgate*, Percy Soc., Early English Poetry, Vol. II (London, 1840), pp. 62-66.

[7] "The Monk Who Honourd the Virgin," in *Originals and Analogues of Some of Chaucer's Canterbury Tales*, ed. F. J. Furnivall et al., Chaucer Soc., 2nd Ser., No. 15 (London, 1888), pp. 286-288.

MacCracken.[8] None of these authors has discussed the background of the tale as a miracle of the Virgin.

Lydgate mentions his source, the *Speculum historiale* of Vincent de Beauvais (ca. 1190–ca. 1264),[9] in the fifth stanza of "The Legend of Dan Joos." It is not certain where Vincent de Beauvais found the story, but Wilson has shown that the first part of the collection of miracles of the Virgin in the *Speculum historiale* was taken from the lost *Mariale magnum*, a collection of miracles of the Virgin made by the Cistercians between 1187 and 1247. Vincent's connection with the Cistercian monastery of Royaumont, where he was lector, or professor of theology for the monks, although he was himself a Dominican, has led Wilson to suggest that the second part of his collection, the part which contains the source of Lydgate's poem, may also have been taken from a Cistercian source.[10]

Lydgate's story is actually a version of the miracle of the Virgin known as "The Monk Who Could Learn Only 'Ave Maria,'" with slight differences in detail. This is one of several legends in which a flower, or some other phenomenon, appears in the mouth or elsewhere about the body of someone who has practiced extraordinary devotion to Our Lady. Among these legends is "The Child Slain by Jews," which Chaucer tells as the "Prioress's Tale" and which also occurs in MS. Vernon. The others, "The Clerk of Chartres," "The Unshriven Clerk," and "The Monk and the Rose-Wreath," are summarized as follows:

"The Clerk of Chartres": A clerk lived a life of wickedness. His one virtue was his habit of praying to the Blessed Virgin. After a violent death, he was buried in a field outside a cemetery. Our Lady, however, appeared to a clerk in the same city and ordered that her servant be given decent burial. When the body was exhumed, a flower was found in the mouth, and the tongue was seen to be preserved from corruption.[11]

"The Unshriven Clerk": A clerk died without the last rites of the Church. He was buried outside a cemetery. Presently, a lily grew from his mouth, as a token of his devotion to Our Lady.[12]

"The Monk and the Rose-Wreath": A Cistercian recited a hundred

[8] *The Minor Poems of John Lydgate*, Part I, EETS, Extra Ser., No. 107 (London, 1911), pp. 311-315.

[9] (Venice, 1494), sig. k4.

[10] *The Stella maris*, pp. 36-44.

[11] Summarized from MS. 12,593 (thirteenth century; fol. 121[b]), Bibliothèque Nationale.

[12] Edited by Tryon, "Miracles of Our Lady," pp. 365-367.

and fifty "Ave Marias" every day. On one occasion, as he rode through a forest on monastery business carrying a sum of money, he said his "Ave Marias" along the way. Some thieves who were about to rob him were restrained by the sight of white doves coming down from Heaven. They gathered roses that fell from his lips at each "Ave" and carried them up to Heaven.[13]

In most accounts of "The Monk and the Rose-Wreath," the Blessed Virgin receives the roses as the monk says his "Aves," and she weaves them into a garland.[14] These tales are all related to the "greyn" motif in the "Prioress's Tale," though they do not explain precisely what Chaucer meant by "greyn."[15]

It is interesting to find that an Abbot Joscio, who may be the person Vincent de Beauvais had in mind when he wrote in his account of the miracle "Erat autem ibidem in Conventu Sancti Bertini quidam monachus Joscio nomine," died at the Abbey of Saint-Bertin in 1163 and was afterward beatified for his exemplary devotion to Our Lady.[16]

ADDITIONAL MS. 39,996

British Museum[1]

This collection of eighteen miracles of the Virgin (foll. 70-80ᵇ) is the largest extant in English, and it must have been even larger since the *mariale* breaks off due to the loss of some leaves after a few lines of the nineteenth tale. Because there is no index, we do not know how its original size may have compared with the size of the Vernon *mariale* in its complete form. Its tales, written in rhymed couplets, are distinctly inferior to the Vernon miracles. The following have been preserved:

1. "How the Devil Seduced a Monk" (here edited).
2. "The Woman Revived for Confession": A woman died without

[13] Summarized from MS. Egerton 117 (fourteenth century; fol. 174) of the British Museum.

[14] For a complete study of the tale, see Joseph Dobner, *Die mittelhochdeutsche Versnovelle Marien Rosenkranz* (Borna-Leipzig, 1928).

[15] For more detailed analysis, see my "The Literary Background of Lydgate's *The Legend of Dan Joos*," *Modern Language Notes*, LXXII (1957), 84-86.

[16] Henri de Laplane, *Les abbés de Saint-Bertin* (Saint-Omer, 1854-55), I, 221, 355; II, 242-243.

[1] Described in British Museum, Department of Manuscripts, *A Catalogue of Additions to the Manuscripts, 1916-1920* (London, 1933), pp. 272-275.

confessing the sins of her youth. Our Lady restored her to life so that she might confess them.

3. "How Our Lady Completed a Chapel": The Blessed Virgin and three of the Holy Innocents appeared to a man who had no money to finish a chapel he had been building. They set to work and helped him to finish it.

4. "The Empress of Rome" (here edited).

5. "How an Abbess Was Delivered"‡. Here told of a prioress. There is no informant, and the bishop does not hear of the scandal.

6. "How a Clerk's Tongue Was Healed": A clerk who had cancer of the tongue was healed by a touch of the Blessed Virgin's finger.

7. "The Jewish Boy"‡.

8. "How a Woman's Son Was Restored to Life": A woman prayed to the Blessed Virgin for a child. Her prayer was granted, but the son born to her died. Again she prayed to Our Lady, and the child was restored to life.

9. "The Devil in Beasts' Shapes": The Devil frightened a drunken monk by assuming the forms of several wild beasts. The Blessed Virgin, however, put the Devil to flight.

10. "The Barns of Jerusalem": During a famine, the monks of an abbey in Jerusalem found their barns miraculously filled. The miracle was attributed to the Blessed Virgin.

11. "The Ring Given to an Image": A youth placed his ring upon the finger of an image of Our Lady. The hand closed upon the ring, which could not then be removed. Afterward, the youth came to his marriage, but the image of the Blessed Virgin reminded him that he had already betrothed himself, so he left his bride and became a monk.

12. "The Broken Tun of Wine": A good woman ordered a tun of wine for the celebration of one of the Blessed Virgin's feasts. The cask broke, spilling the wine. Because she was sorry for the woman, the Blessed Virgin caused the cask to be mended and the contents restored.

13. "The Feast of Our Lady's Nativity": A man heard angels singing "Ave Maria" in a field at the same time every year. When he prayed for an explanation, he learned that it was the anniversary of the nativity of Mary. The man informed his bishop, who obtained authorization from the pope to establish this feast.

14. "How Some Jews Tried to Efface a Holy Picture": Some Jews tried to remove from a wall a portrait of the Blessed Virgin. No substance known to them was able to remove it.

15. "The Woman Who Committed Incest": The Devil disguised himself as a lawyer and appeared at the trial of a woman who had committed incest. But the Blessed Virgin also appeared at the trial, in order that the woman might have justice. When the Devil recognized his enemy, he disappeared.

16. "The Jew Who Insulted Our Lady's Image": A Jew who tried to defile an image of the Blessed Virgin was suddenly struck dead.

17. "The Merchant's Surety"‡.

18. "The Unshriven Clerk"‡.[2]

The only theory that has been offered as to the source of this *mariale* is that of Tryon, who has suggested that it was based upon the *Stella maris*.[3] This opinion rests upon two circumstances, though Tryon notes that she had not read the *Stella maris* at the time when her article was written. First, the tales do indeed occur in the *Stella maris*.[4] Second, the miracles of the Virgin as they appear in both are unusually brief. In particular, the details of the English miracles are inclined to differ considerably from any known versions of the same stories. As to the first observation, experience with this kind of narrative shows that repetitiousness is one of its chief characteristics. The same tales turn up again and again, especially in the really large *mariales*. The second observation (the brevity common to both collections) is irrelevant. Some of the poems in the *Stella maris* are so short that they would be pointless unless the reader already knew the stories to which they allude. There is no substantial evidence for Tryon's theory, though the comparisons she shows are interesting.

How the Devil Seduced a Monk[5]

Nothing is known about the background of this tale.

The Empress of Rome[6]

This miracle of the Virgin is important as an analogue of the story of Constance told by Chaucer's Man of Law (ca. 1390). The details, of course, are widely different. The woes of Constance are on two occasions due to the machinations of wicked mothers-in-law, while the Empress of Rome is the victim of a brother-in-law's lust. The murder

---

[2] Editions: Tryon, "Miracles of Our Lady," (2-3) pp. 344-346, (5-18) pp. 349-367.
[3] "Miracles of Our Lady," pp. 340-341.
[4] Tryon gives a table showing the comparisons, p. 341.
[5] Edited by Tryon, pp. 342-344.
[6] Edited by Tryon, pp. 346-349.

of which Constance is unjustly accused is that of her benefactor's wife; the Empress of Rome is accused of murdering the children she has been employed to nurse. Chaucer's heroine, moreover, is falsely accused of giving birth to a monster, and she is not given the power of curing leprosy, which ultimately brings about the recognition of the Empress of Rome by her husband and their consequent reconciliation. Margaret Schlauch's *Chaucer's Constance and Accused Queens* reveals that both stories are assembled from a stock of motifs gathered from a group of *Märchen* known to folklorists as the *Crescentia-Florentia-Hildegard* cycle.[7]

The antiquity of the presentation of this story as a miracle of the Virgin cannot be ascertained, but it occurs at least as early as the second half of the twelfth century in a *mariale* belonging to MS. 14,463 of the Bibliothèque Nationale, where it is given as the forty-fifth tale. The source of Chaucer's narrative is thought to be the tale of Constance in Nicholas Trivet's Anglo-Norman chronicle (ca. 1335),[8] but the fact that Gower gives the same legend in his *Confessio amantis* (Book II, lines 587-1598),[9] written in the early 1390's, has led to some controversy about the possible relation of his story to Chaucer's (and thus to Nicholas Trivet's).[10] Also debatable is the possibility that Chaucer knew the tale as a miracle of the Virgin. Certainly, there are some Marian references in the poem, but it does not appear that Chaucer meant to attribute the salvation of Constance to a miracle wrought by Our Lady.

MS. RAWLINSON POETRY 225

Bodleian Library[1]

Theophilus

The legend of "Theophilus" was originally Greek. It is particularly important as an analogue of the Faust story. The only clue to the

---

[7] (New York, 1927.)

[8] *The Life of Constance*, ed. Edmund Brock, in *Originals and Analogues of Some of Chaucer's Canterbury Tales*, ed. F. J. Furnivall et al., Chaucer Soc., 2nd Ser., No. 7 (London, 1872), pp. 1-53.

[9] Edited by G. C. Macaulay, *The English Works of John Gower*, Vol. I, EETS, Extra Ser., No. 81 (London, 1900), pp. 146-173.

[10] Robinson, *The Works of Geoffrey Chaucer*, p. 690.

---

[1] Described by Falconer Madan, *A Summary Catalogue of Western Manuscripts in the Bodleian Library at Oxford*, III (Oxford, 1895), 334.

authorship of the tale may be found in two Greek manuscripts: Coislin 283 of the Bibliothèque Nationale, possibly as late as the eleventh century, and Palat. gr. 3 of the Nationalbibliothek, Vienna, which is older but of uncertain date.[2] These manuscripts, which give the same account of the miracle, are called "Eutychian Manuscripts," because the Vienna manuscript contains a postscript by one Eutychianos, who claims to be not only a member of the household of Theophilus but an eyewitness of the events described.

The tale is also found in a Latin translation of the ninth century, attributed to Paulus Diaconus of Naples.[3] Its first known appearance thereafter in the literature of western Europe is the "Lapsus et conversio Theophili vicedomini," written by the Saxon nun Hroswitha of Gandersheim in the tenth century.[4] The earliest account of the miracle in English is the prose summary given by the Anglo-Saxon bishop Aelfric (ca. 955–ca. 1020) in one of his sermons.[5] It later occurs in *The South English Legendary* and in some manuscripts of *The North English Homily Collection*.

The Rawlinson version of this widely known miracle of the Virgin differs radically from every other known to scholars. Because the English poet made extensive use of dialogue, often without connecting text, both Wilhelm Heuser, who was the first to edit the poem,[6] and Karl Plenzat[7] have seen in it traces of a dramatic original, perhaps the one by Rutebeuf. It seems more likely, however, that its peculiarities are merely characteristics of the Middle English tail-rhyme romances. The poem begins, in the manner typical of this kind of writing, with a bid for the reader's attention. This is followed, also typically, by a list of the protagonist's accomplishments, which contains many of the cliché phrases found in these romances. Equally characteristic is the otherworld adventure, in which the hero is sought out by a necromancer or some denizen of the other world (in this case by the Jew) who introduces him to the Devil. A thorough discussion of the tail-

[2] Both texts are edited by Ludwig Radermacher, "Griechische Quellen zur Faustsage," *Sitzungsberichte der kaiserlichen Akademie der Wissenschaften in Wien, Phil.-hist. Klasse*, CCVI (1927), Fasc. iv, 182-219.

[3] *Acta sanctorum . . . notis illustravit Joannes Bollandus*, February, Vol. I (Antwerp, 1658), pp. 483-487. See also Philip M. Palmer and Robert P. More, *The Sources of the Faust Tradition* (New York, 1936), pp. 60-75.

[4] In *Hrotsvithae opera*, ed. Strecker, pp. 67-80.

[5] "De assumptione beate Mariae," in *The Homilies of the Anglo-Saxon Church*, Part I, p. 448.

[6] "Eine neue mittelenglische Version der Theophilus-Sage," *Englische Studien*, XXXII (1903), 1-23.

[7] "Die Theophiluslegende in den Dichtungen des Mittelalters," *Germanische Studien*, XLIII (1926), 88.

rhyme romances and their literary characteristics may be found in A. McI. Trounce's "The English Tail-Rhyme Romances."[8] Since this poem has so many of them, it is not necessary to look further for an explanation of its peculiarities.[9]

MS. 432

Lambeth Palace Library[1]

The Fool of Alexandria

This manuscript is a miscellany of religious pieces. It contains (foll. 85-90) fifteen miracles of the Virgin in prose. They are:

1. "The Fool of Alexandria" (here edited).
2. "Our Lady's Hand and the Scales of Justice": A sinner came to his judgment, and when it appeared that the Devil would gain his soul, he prayed to the Blessed Virgin. She came and laid her hand on the scale where his few good deeds were being weighed, and thus she delivered his soul.
3. "A Drop of Blood and the Scales of Justice": The Blessed Virgin prayed to her son for one drop of the sacred blood, and this weighed so much that the soul of a hopeless sinner was saved.
4. "The Woman Who Swallowed a Spider": A woman committed incest with her brother and then tried to kill herself by swallowing a spider. When death approached, she cried out to Our Lady, who first admonished her for her sins and then healed her. The woman afterward lived in prayer and penance.
5. "The Man of Norwich": Two Dominicans converted a man of Norwich, who nevertheless failed to confess his sins. One night, the man dreamed that a hand was suffocating him, and a voice warned him to make his confession. When he prayed to Our Lady, she set him free to do so.
6. "The Blind Boy of Westminster": At Westminster, on the Feast of St. Peter and St. Paul, a poor woman wept by the Blessed Virgin's altar, with her son who had been blind from birth. Suddenly, she

---

[8] *Medium Aevum*, I (1932), 87-108, 168-182; II (1933), 34-57.
[9] See my "The Rawlinson Version of *Theophilus*," *Modern Language Notes*, LXXI (1956), 556-559.

---

[1] Described by M. R. James and Claude Jenkins, *A Descriptive Catalogue of the Manuscripts in the Library of Lambeth Palace* (Cambridge, Eng., 1930-32). pp. 599-601.

rose and told the sacristan that a vision had appeared to her in which she had been told to wash the statue of the Virgin and Child and to bathe the blind child with the water. When the sacristan did this, the child was given his sight.

7. "The Waxen Image for Roc-Amadour": A man made a waxen image of his dying son to send to the shrine of Roc-Amadour. Intending that the wax should be the same weight as the child, he placed it upon a scale. At this moment, the child was cured.

8. "The Child Willed to the Devil": With the consent of her husband, a woman made a vow of chastity, but the man afterward violated her vow, and she willed to the Devil the child she had conceived. She bore a son, and when he was twelve years old, the Devil appeared and demanded his due. When the child learned the secret of his birth, he went to the pope, who sent him to a series of holy men to ask for advice. Finally, he went to stay with a hermit, who told him to pray to the Blessed Virgin until the day which the Devil had set to claim his soul. On that day, he sat between the hermit and the altar at which the hermit was saying his mass. At the "Pater noster," the Devil carried him off to Hell, but the Blessed Virgin rescued him before the "Pax Domini." Then the hermit gave him his blessing and sent him to comfort his friends.

9. "The Clerk of Lichfield": A clerk of Lichfield, who loved St. Anne, always added to his "Ave Maria" the words "Et benedicta sit sancta tua mater Anna." As he lay sick, his friends heard him exclaim that St. Anne and the Blessed Virgin were appearing to him in a vision.

10. "The Woman Tempted by the Devil in the Guise of a Man": The Devil, in the guise of a man, tempted a woman to sin. She consulted a hermit about her temptation. He taught her to say "St. Mary, help me!" at every onslaught of temptation. These words drove the Devil away.

11. "The Monk Who Could Learn Only 'Ave Maria' "‡.

12. "The Child Caught by the Tide": A woman taught her child to say "Ave Maria" whenever he was afraid. One day, while playing by the sea with his friends, he was caught by the tide. Terrified, he said his "Ave Maria." Then a beautiful lady led him safely to shore.

13. "How a Woman Counted Her 'Aves' ": A nun taught her cousin to count her "Aves" upon her knuckles. When the cousin died, she appeared to the nun in a vision, her hands shining with jewels in the places where she had counted her "Aves."

14. "The Death of John of Bellavilla": When Abbot John of Bellavilla lay dying, he admonished his monks to pray often to Our Lady. They

afterward found out that he had had visions of the Blessed Virgin holding her child in her arms.

15. " 'Ave Benigne Jesu' ": As a woman was saying her "Ave Maria" before an image of the Blessed Virgin, she heard a voice telling her to say first of all "Ave Benigne Jesu."

These miracles of the Virgin are short summaries, not fully developed literary works. The source of the collection, first edited by Horstmann,[2] is not known, but analogues of "The Fool of Alexandria" are found in the writings of Etienne de Bourbon (d. ca. 1261),[3] and also in the Old French "Dit des trois chanoins."[4]

WILLIAM CAXTON

Golden Legend[1]

Caxton explains, in the preface to his English version of the *Legenda aurea*, that his immediate sources are three legendaries—in French, in Latin, and in English—and that these differ among themselves. His work has made them into one book. This means that his *Golden Legend* is not strictly a translation from Jacobus de Voragine. Its legends do not all appear in the Latin manuscripts of the *Legenda aurea*.

How the Feast of Our Lady's Conception Was Established

The story here edited, despite its English origin, is one that is found in the *Legenda aurea*.[2] Also, it is found in the *TS* series of miracles of

[2] "Prosalegenden," *Anglia*, III (1880), 320-325.

[3] In Albert Lecoy de la Marche, ed. *Anecdotes historiques, légendes et apologues* (Paris, 1877), pp. 151-153.

[4] In Achille Jubinal, ed. *Nouveau recueil de contes, dits, fabliaux et autres pièces inédites des XIIIe, XIVe et XVe siècles*, I (Paris, 1839), 266-282.

[1] Here edited from a copy of the first edition, Westminster [1483], which is a fragment, in the Henry E. Huntington Library. References to other miracles of the Virgin in Caxton's *Golden Legend* are from the second edition, [Westminster, 1487?], which is a mixed edition in all the known copies. Both are described by Edward Gordon Duff, *Fifteenth Century English Books* ([London], 1917), pp. 113-114, items 408 and 409. A Modern English edition is that of Frederick S. Ellis, *The Golden Legend or Lives of the Saints as Englished by William Caxton* (London, 1931). "How the Feast of Our Lady's Conception Was Established" appears in Ellis, II, 126-128.

[2] Ed. Graesse, pp. 869-870.

the Virgin which Southern has attributed to Anselm the Younger and in the Edinburgh manuscript of *The North English Homily Collection*. The fact that Archbishop Anselm of Canterbury is reported to be the narrator may explain how the younger Anselm happened to include it in his *mariale*, but there is no evidence for this.

More important is the fact that the vision of Abbot Helisius, whose name is also reported as Elsinus and as Aelsi (which was his English name), while itself outside the province of historical investigation is nevertheless attached to a person whose identity is authenticated by documentary evidence. Southern, in his investigation of the miracles in *TS*, found that this man was indeed Abbot of Ramsey at the time of the Norman Conquest. He was abbot there in 1080 and in 1088, the year of his death.[3]

Caxton used a large number of the miracles of the Virgin that were in his sources. It is difficult to obtain an exact count of the tales, because in this famous legendary, as in others, some saints' lives contain incidents in which Our Lady appears without being a central figure, and there are no criteria by which to determine whether all these incidents, or only some, should be considered miracles of the Virgin as such. The problem does not arise in connection with versified legendaries, largely because there is less tendency to digression in verse than in prose, and also because there is less tendency to consider a few lines of verse apart from their context. This is the reason why the life of St. Mary of Egypt as it occurs in *The South English Legendary*[4] is not listed as a miracle of the Virgin, even though the part of her story which deals with Our Lady's role in her conversion occurs frequently in prose *mariales*. Because Caxton's book is important, and because the miracles of the Virgin in it are likely to have been widely known in one form or another in medieval England, it has seemed necessary to summarize all of them, though most are too short and too pedestrian in style to warrant editing them here. This, of course, sets a precedent, and the miracles of the Virgin scattered through other prose works will be dealt with in the same manner throughout the present study. A list of the miracles of the Virgin according to Caxton follows (with signatures of the [1487?] edition); the volume and page references are to F. S. Ellis' edition.

1. "Octavian and the Sybil": The Emperor Octavian, when the state wished to deify him, sent for a sybil to find out whether anyone

---

[3] "The English Origins," pp. 194-198.
[4] Horstmann, ed. *The Early South-English Legendary*, pp. 260-271.

would be born greater than he. She had a vision of a woman and child standing in the sun (sig. a5; I, 27).

2. "How the Feast of Our Lady's Conception Was Established" (here edited).

3. "The Clerk Who Forgot Our Lady's Hours": A clerk who loved Our Lady and said her hours every day took a bride and forgot to say the hours before the wedding. After the ceremony he remembered this, sent the bridal party home ahead of him, and stayed behind to say his prayers. When he came to the anthem "Pulchra es," Our Lady appeared to him and asked if he had found another fairer than she. Then she told him to leave his bride and to consecrate himself to her, and after that she admonished him to hallow the feast of her conception on December 8, promising him that she would be his bride in Heaven (sig. m3; II, 128-129).

4. "Julian the Apostate": The Emperor Julian threatened to destroy the city of Caesarea because of a quarrel with St. Basil. St. Basil afterward had a vision in which Our Lady sent a warrior to fight for her, and Julian fell in battle (sig. r2; III, 15-16).

5. "The Feast of Our Lady's Purification" (sig. r4ᵛ; III, 25-26) ‡.

6. "How Our Lady's Image Ended the Plague": During an outbreak of plague, St. Gregory carried in procession an image of Our Lady made by St. Luke. The plague ceased at once (sig. s6; III, 64-65).

7. "The Monk Who Could Learn Only 'Ave Maria'" (sig. t6; III, 100-101) ‡.

8. "The Devil in Service" (sig. t6ʳ⁻ᵛ; III, 101-102) ‡.

9. "The Conversion of Mary of Egypt": St. Mary, a holy recluse in Egypt, told a hermit named Zosimus the story of her conversion, which occurred after she had been a prostitute for seventeen years. In Jerusalem, she had tried to enter a church, but an invisible force had blocked her entry. She had realized the enormity of her sins and prayed to Our Lady, who had then allowed her to enter the church (sig. t7ᵛ; III, 107-108).

10. "The Nun of Florence": On the day of the martyrdom of St. Peter of Milan, a nun of Florence had a vision in which she saw Our Lady rise into Heaven, with the soul of St. Peter beside her (sig. x2ᵛ; III, 154).

11. "How St. Leo's Hand Was Restored": As St. Leo distributed Holy Communion, he began to lust after a woman who had kissed his hand. Despising himself, he cut off the hand she had kissed and was afterward unable any more to say mass. Then Our Lady came and restored his hand (sig. A1ᵛ; IV, 10).

12. "The Priest of One Mass": A simple priest could say no mass but that of Our Lady. For this, St. Thomas of Canterbury suspended him. Forbidden to say mass, he prayed to Our Lady, who then appeared to him in a vision. She sent him to St. Thomas, commanding him to tell the prelate that she had embroidered his hair shirt as a sign. Recognizing his mistake, St. Thomas restored the man to his office (sig. B4ᵛ; IV, 58-59).

13. "The Pilgrim of St. James" (sig. C7ᵛ; IV, 106-108) ‡.

14. "The Monk of St. Peter's at Cologne": Although he died in his sins, a monk of St. Peter's Monastery at Cologne obtained mercy through his patron saint, who prayed for him to Our Lady. Through her intercession, he was restored to life so that he could do penance (sig. E4; IV, 163-164).

15. "How the World Was Entrusted to the Dominicans": Before the establishment of the Order of Preachers, a monk saw in a vision Our Lady appeal to her son for the salvation of the world. Instead of punishing it, Our Lord decided to entrust it to the Order of Preachers (sigs. E7ᵛ-8; IV, 178-179).

16. "Three Spears": A Franciscan beheld in a vision Our Lady interceding with her son, who was about to destroy the world with three spears, symbols of its pride, luxury, and avarice. When asked who might be capable of conquering these vices, she presented St. Francis and St. Dominic (sig. E8; IV, 179-180).

17. "St. Dominic and the Sick Man": A prelate of some note decided to enter the Order of Preachers. He fell sick before he could do so. When St. Dominic prayed for him to Our Lady, she appeared to the sick man in a vision, cured him, and showed him the religious habit the order was to adopt (sig. F1; IV, 183-185).

18. "Stephen, the Wicked Judge": In Rome, there was a wicked judge, so corrupt that he wrested land from churches. In particular, he took away property belonging to St. Laurence and to St. Agnes. After his death, these saints punished him, and St. Laurence injured his arm. Only after his patron saint, St. Projecte, interceded for him with Our Lady did he win mercy in Heaven: he was restored to life in order to do penance. Then he discovered that his arm was damaged as if by fire (sig. F8ᵛ; IV, 218-219).

19. "Peter the Carter": On the Feast of St. Mary Magdalene, a carter named Peter yoked his oxen and began to curse them. The team was struck down in a sudden storm, and Peter's leg was so badly injured that it fell off. He hid the limb in a hole and prayed to Our Lady for help. She appeared to him in a vision, accompanied by St. Hippolitus,

whom she instructed to restore the missing leg. Peter, however, was lame for a year afterward, until he had another vision in which St. Hippolitus completed the cure. The Devil then tempted Peter in the guise of a nude woman. He overcame his lust by girding himself with a priest's stole. The Devil fled, leaving behind the carcass of a dead woman (sigs. G3ᵛ-4; IV, 232-233).

20. "How Chartres Was Saved" (sig. G6; IV, 242) ‡.

21. "St. Elizabeth's Vision of the Assumption": In one of her visions, St. Elizabeth beheld a bright light around a tomb. Angels bore from it the body of the Virgin Mary and carried it up to Heaven (sig. G6; IV, 242-243).

22. "The Monk Who Consoled Our Lady": In sorrow for Our Lady's suffering because of the wounds of Christ, a monk said every day a prayer beginning "Rejoice thee, Virgin and mother undefiled." On his deathbed, he had a vision in which Our Lady wished him the joy of Heaven (sig. G7; IV, 247).

23. "The Drowned Sacristan" (sig. G7ʳ⁻ᵛ; IV, 247-248) ‡.

24. "How Our Lady Came to the Devil Instead of the Victim" (sigs. G7ᵛ-8; IV, 248-251) ‡.

25. "Our Lady's Hand and the Scales of Justice" (sig. G8ʳ⁻ᵛ; IV, 251-252) ‡.

26. "The Jewish Boy" (sig. G8ᵛ; IV, 252-253) ‡.

27. "The Gossiping Monks": Some monks who were engaged in idle conversation by a riverbank heard the oars of some devils who were bearing off to Hell the soul of an unfaithful monk. Frightened by this, they cried out to Our Lady and thereby saved themselves from the same fate (sig. G8ᵛ; IV, 253).

28. "The Woman Tempted by the Devil in the Guise of a Man" (sig. G8ᵛ; IV, 253-254) ‡.

29. "The Feast of Our Lady's Nativity" (sigs. L4ᵛ-5; V, 103-104) ‡.

30. "The Election of Pope Celestine": When Gregory IX died, the conclave of cardinals was unable to decide who should be his successor. They vowed to Our Lady that they would establish the celebration of the octave day of the Feast of her Nativity if she would help them to reach an agreement. Having done this, they reached agreement, and Celestine was elected pope (sig. L5; V, 104).

31. "The Knight of Kirkby": A knight on his way to a tournament stopped to hear mass in honor of Our Lady and lingered so long that he missed his tournament. As he rode out from the church, his friends congratulated him for deeds of honor that had been miraculously performed in his absence (sig. L5; V, 105).

32. "The Bishop's Vision": A bishop who loved Our Lady had a vision in which she escorted him singing into church (sig. L5; V, 105-106).

33. "The Woman Who Stole Our Lady's Child": A woman whose son had been taken prisoner prayed to Our Lady for his release. When her prayers were not answered, she decided to show Our Lady how she felt, and she stole the image of the child from her shrine in a church. Then Our Lady obtained the release of the woman's son, and after that the woman gave back the image she had stolen (sig. L5; V, 106-107).

34. "The Thief Saved from the Gallows": A thief, hanged for his crimes, was sustained for three days upon the gallows because he had prayed to Our Lady. Afterward, his executioners tried to cut his throat, but Our Lady saved him. Realizing the situation, the executioners let him go, and he became a monk (sig. L5; V, 107).

35. "The Clerk Who Forgot Our Lady's Hours" (sig. L5ᵛ; V, 108) ‡. The Feast of Our Lady's Conception is not mentioned.

36. "The Priest of One Mass" (sigs. L5ᵛ-6; V, 108-109) ‡. St. Thomas of Canterbury is not mentioned.

37. "The Wicked Clerk's Vision of Judgment": A wicked clerk, who nevertheless prayed to Our Lady, had a vision in which he was brought to his judgment. He received the sentence of damnation, but he was saved by Our Lady's intercession so that he could amend his life (sig. L6; V, 109).

38. "Theophilus" (sig. L6; V, 109-110) ‡.

39. "St. Jerome's *Responsorium*": St. Jerome went into a church and passed a statue of Our Lady as he went to pray at the shrines of other saints. He did the same thing as he left, whereupon Our Lady asked for an explanation. Then he knelt and composed the *responsorium* "Sancta et immaculata virginitas" (sig. L6ᵛ; V, 111).

40. "The Death of St. Clare": At the time of the death of St. Clare, Our Lady appeared with a company of virgins and placed a rich mantle upon her (sigs. U6ᵛ-7; VI, 166).

41. "The Ring Given to an Image" (sig. aa5ᵛ; VI, 232) ‡. Here told of St. Edmund. There is no marriage incident after the youth has betrothed himself to Our Lady.

42. "The Marriage of St. Katherine": A hermit named Adrian had a vision in which Our Lady instructed him to call Katherine, a pagan maiden, to behold her divine bridegroom. Katherine was converted to Christianity, and Our Lady became her godmother. Katherine afterward became the bride of Christ (sigs. bb8ᵛ-cc2; VII, 9-15).

MS. ASHMOLE 61

Bodleian Library[1]

The Good Knight and His Jealous Wife

Nothing is known about the background of this poem, which ends abruptly at line 396 due to the loss of the leaf on which it originally concluded. The only earlier edition of the poem is that of Horstmann.[2]

This edition differs from Horstmann's chiefly in the interpretation of the terminal flourishes in the handwriting, which is of the very late fifteenth century or the early sixteenth. Horstmann has assumed that the scribe meant most terminal flourishes as final *e*'s, and he has supplied them. He has also assumed that the thin horizontal line which appears erratically over many words in the text implies that *m* or *n* should be added, or, when it occurs over a final consonant, that final *e* should be added. This, however, cannot be the case in many instances, and these features seem to have been merely peculiarities of the scribal handwriting most of the time. In the present edition, therefore, only the reflex curve on final *r* has been interpreted to mean final *e* and only a horizontal line over a final vowel to mean that *m* or *n* should be added. In an earlier manuscript, the rhyme words would be of some assistance in expanding abbreviations, but we have here no assurance that the scribe pronounced final *e* with any degree of consistency, if indeed he pronounced it at all.

The poem seems to have been composed earlier (probably in the fourteenth century) and to have been tampered with by the scribe. Evidence of this can be seen in lines 160-161, where *yow* now occurs instead of the obvious rhyme *the*. The vocabulary of the poem is basically Northern, though many of the grammatical forms have been altered.

---

[1] Described by William Henry Black, *A Descriptive, Analytical, and Critical Catalogue of the Manuscripts Bequeathed unto the University of Oxford by Elias Ashmole*, in Oxford University, Bodleian Library, *Catalogi codicum manuscriptorum*, Part 10 (Oxford, 1845), pp. 106-107.

[2] *Altenglische Legenden*, pp. 329-333.

APPENDIXES

I

John Mirk's *Festial*

A. Prose miracles of the Virgin in John Mirk's *Festial* (ca. 1415), summarized from *Mirk's Festial* edited by Theodor Erbe in 1905 from MS. Gough Eccl. Top. 4 (Summary Catalogue No. 17,680) of the Bodleian Library. Page references are to Erbe's edition.

1. "The Monk and the Rose-Wreath" (pp. 16-17) ‡. Here told of a reeve. Our Lady gathered the roses that fell from his lips at each "Ave" and placed them in a garland which she had set upon his head.
2. "How the Feast of Our Lady's Conception Was Established" (p. 17) ‡.
3. "Salome's Hands": St. Joseph brought two midwives to tend Our Lady—Yebel, who believed in her virginity, and Salome, who did not. Salome's hands shriveled up when she touched Our Lady. When an angel bid her touch the child, however, her hands were restored (pp. 22-23).
4. "St. Dunstan's Mother": Before St. Dunstan's birth, his mother went to church on Candlemas. When the procession began, every candle was extinguished. Then a light from Heaven came to kindle hers, and all the others were lighted from it (p. 60).
5. "The Feast of Our Lady's Purification" (pp. 60-61) ‡.
6. "One Good Deed": A woman died, having done no good deed in her life except establish a fund to keep a candle burning before Our Lady's image in a church. When her soul was being carried off to Hell, the angels protested because of the candle. When Our Lady ruled that the candle be left to comfort those in Hell, the fiends preferred to leave the woman behind. She was then restored to life in order that she might make amends for her sins (pp. 61-62).
7. "Three Spears" (p. 73) ‡.
8. "The Death of Robert Grosseteste": When Robert Grosseteste lay dying, fiends from Hell nearly turned him from the Faith, until the Blessed Virgin appeared to him and instructed him to say that he believed all that the Church believed. With that, the fiends vanished (p. 78).
9. "Perys": A man named Perys died, having done no good deed in his life except fling a loaf of bread to a beggar. For this small thing alone, Our Lady prayed for him, and he was restored to life so that he might live in virtue (p. 104).

139

10. "The Lily in the Wine Pot": A Jew declared that he would not believe in the Immaculate Conception unless a lily sprang forth from a nearby wine pot. As he spoke, this very thing happened (pp. 108-109).

11. "The Five Joys": A holy maiden, who had often said prayers in honor of the Five Joys of Our Lady, feared Hell as she was dying. Our Lady appeared to her and promised her everlasting joy (p. 110).

12. "How Our Lady's Milk Healed a Monk's Throat" (p. 110) ‡. Here told of Fulbert of Chartres.

13. "The Woman Tempted by the Devil in the Guise of a Man" (p. 226) ‡.

14. "The Jewish Boy" (p. 227) ‡.

15. "The Clerk Who Would See Our Lady" (p. 234) ‡.

16. "The Feast of Our Lady's Nativity" (p. 247) ‡.

17. "The Woman Who Stole Our Lady's Child" (pp. 247-248) ‡.

18. "The Jew of France": A Jew of France, passing from Bristow to Wilton, was robbed and abandoned in an old house. Our Lady came and released him. She showed him a vision of Hell, and the Jew was converted to Christ (pp. 248-249).

B. Additional miracles of the Virgin in Erbe's edition that may not be genuine parts of Mirk's *Festial*. The first is from MS. Cotton Claudius A.ii (ca. 1450) and the second from MS. Harley 2,403 (fifteenth century), both in the British Museum.

1. "Eulalia": A nun of Shaftesbury, named Eulalia, was in the habit of saying a hundred and fifty "Ave Marias" every day, but she said them so fast that Our Lady came and reproached her. She then told Eulalia to say only half the number but these very devoutly (pp. 299-300).

2. "How Our Lady Restored a Scribe's Hand": The Emperor of Rome employed a famous scribe to teach his kinsman how to write. When the kinsman became skilled, he grew jealous of his teacher's fame and sought to destroy him. He forged a treasonable letter, and when the scribe was unable to prove his innocence, the Emperor had his hand cut off. Our Lady, however, came and healed the scribe, and the Emperor punished the guilty student. The scribe afterward painted a picture of the Virgin and Child which miraculously came to life in order to convert a Jew (pp. 301-303).

II

An Alphabet of Tales

Prose miracles of the Virgin in the fifteenth-century English translation of the *Alphabetum narrationum* (formerly attributed to Etienne de Besançon and to Arnold of Liège), in Additional MS. 25,719 (mid-fifteenth century) of the British Museum. Summarized from Mary Macleod Banks, ed. *An Alphabet of Tales*, Early English Text Society, Original Series, Nos. 126, 127 (London, 1904-05). Page references are to this edition.

1. "How an Abbess Was Delivered" (pp. 11-12) ‡.
2. "The Monk Who Could Learn Only 'Ave Maria' " (p. 53) ‡.
3. "The Devil in Service" (pp. 53-54) ‡.
4. "Our Lady's Elixir": A Cistercian was so busy with his duties as a leech that he neglected his devotions. During matins on one of Our Lady's feasts, he saw the Blessed Virgin feeding his fellow monks with a wonderful elixir. He received none, since she accused him of taking too much comfort in his art. Thereafter, the monk took his duties seriously, and on one of Our Lady's feasts he was given the elixir (pp. 135-136).
5. "The Christ Child as a Reward": A Cistercian prayed for some knowledge of the reward awaiting those who carry their cross in this life. In a vision he saw Our Lady holding her child in her arms. She gave him to all those who had accepted the cross (p. 160).
6. "The Woman Tempted by the Devil in the Guise of a Man" (pp. 178-179) ‡. Here told of a priest's mistress who had turned from her evil life to become a nun. The Devil was put to flight by the words "Ave Maria."
7. "Three Spears (p. 193) ‡.
8. "St. Dominic and the Sick Man" (p. 194) ‡.
9. "The Lazy Monk": A monk who was so lazy that he neglected his duties fell asleep against a tree. Our Lady appeared to him and admonished him. When he awoke, he saw the back of a departing woman (p. 197).
10. "The Jewish Boy" (pp. 210-211) ‡.
11. "The Woman Who Committed Incest" (pp. 220-222) ‡.
12. "The Stonemason's Fortune": A hermit who took shelter briefly at the home of a stonemason was so impressed with the man's charity that he prayed for his prosperity. The man afterward found a bag of gold, went to court as a rich man, and became a bailiff. He then

went about oppressing the poor. The hermit prayed to Our Lady, and soon thereafter the mason fell from favor and returned to his former way of life (pp. 226-227).

13. "How Our Lady Kissed a Dying Monk": A dying Cistercian told a brother that Our Lady had appeared to him, kissed him, and informed him that his death was seven days off (pp. 250-251).

14. "How Our Lady Restored a Scribe's Hand" (pp. 262-264) ‡. Here told of St. John Damascene. There is no mention of the miraculous picture.

15. "Stephen, the Wicked Judge" (p. 297) ‡.

16. "How St. Leo's Hand Was Restored" (pp. 298-299) ‡.

17. "The Knight of Kirkby" (p. 315) ‡.

18. "The Woman Who Stole Our Lady's Child" (pp. 315-316) ‡.

19. "The Thief Saved from the Gallows" (p. 316) ‡.

20. "The Clerk Who Forgot Our Lady's Hours" (p. 317) ‡.

21. "Theophilus" (pp. 318-319) ‡.

22. "Beatrice the Sacristan": Beatrice the sacristan ran away with a clerk, who afterward abandoned her. She wandered about for fifteen years and then returned to find that Our Lady had taken her place (pp. 319-320).

23. "How the Devil, in the Guise of a Fair Woman, Appeared to an Anchoress": An anchoress desired to behold Our Lady, and the Devil appeared to her in the guise of a fair woman. Her confessor told her to say "Ave Maria" to the vision, and the Devil vanished when she did so (pp. 320-321).

24. "The Nun Tempted by the World": A nun said "Ave Maria" every time she was tempted to leave the convent. On the day she failed to do this, temptation finally overcame her (p. 321).

25. "How Our Lady's Image Ended the Plague" (pp. 321-322) ‡.

26. "Octavian and the Sybil" (pp. 369-370) ‡.

27. "The Knight Who Refused to Abjure Our Lady": A knight, who had wasted all his goods, struck a bargain with the Devil but refused to abjure Our Lady. He afterward prayed before an image of the Virgin and Child, whereupon the image of Our Lady knelt to the infant and obtained pardon for the knight (pp. 370-372).

28. "The Ring Given to an Image" (pp. 438-439) ‡. The youth put his ring on Our Lady's finger while playing handball near a church.

29. "The Empress of Rome" (pp. 447-450) ‡.

30. "The Priest of One Mass" (p. 508) ‡.

31. "Julian the Apostate" (pp. 515-516) ‡.

III

Two Fragments in Verse

The Wicked Knight and the Friar

MS. Thornton (MS. A.5.2; ca. 1440; foll. 147-148), Lincoln Cathedral Chapter Library.[1]

Only the beginning and the end of this miracle of the Virgin have survived. It is impossible to discover from the fragments what tale was originally told, though the incipit, "De miraculo beate Marie," leaves no doubt that the poem was a miracle of the Virgin. The stanzas are in tail-rhyme, and the dialect is Northern. The remains of the poem have been edited by Horstmann.[2]

The Child and the Abbot

MS. Harley 2,380 (late fifteenth or early sixteenth century; foll. 74^b-78), British Museum.[3]

This badly mutilated text is the only version extant in English of a legend telling how a little boy shared his food with the Christ Child and how the Christ Child in turn invited him to dine. The scribe has added to our difficulties by writing parts of the text in the margins with the page turned about, and the writing is so crowded that it cannot be deciphered. Tryon has salvaged all of the readable text in her edition of it, but this is not enough to tell us exactly what happened in the story.[4] A bibliography of analogues of the legend is given by Wilson.[5]

---

[1] Described by Reginald Maxwell Woolley, *Catalogue of the Manuscripts of Lincoln Cathedral Chapter Library* (London, 1927), pp. 51-61.

[2] *Altenglische Legenden*, pp. 503-504.

[3] Described in British Museum, Department of Manuscripts, *A Catalogue of the Harleian Manuscripts in the British Museum*, II (London, 1808), 675.

[4] "Miracles of Our Lady," pp. 378-386.

[5] *The Stella maris*, p. 199.

INDEX

Date Due

JA 22 66		
OCT 13 1983		